Fischer • Jerry Fischer • John Fisher • Debra Flammond • Eunice Flanagan • [...] nery • Carol Flattum • Michael Fleming • Jim Fletcher • Suzanne Fletcher • Ian Flitcrof[...] ontaine • Suzanne (Erickson) Fontenault • John Forbes • Eugene Fosnight • Becky (Hol[...] Linda (Doering) Fountain • James Fox • Julee Frakes • Joe Francica • Donell Frankma[...] Freier • James Frerk • Alan Frevik • Connie Frewaldt • Phil Friesen • Heidi Fritschel • Joyce Fry • Ye (Arlene) Fu • Michael Fuerst • Cynthia Fuhs • Michael Furlow • Sablou Gabriel • Joanne Gabrynowicz • Carolyn (VanBeek) Gacke • Ken Gacke • Timothy Gadd • Gary Gage • Anita Galkin • Carrie Gallap • Kevin Gallo • Patricia Gannon • Daniel Gapp • Gabriella Garcia • Peter Gardner • Tim Gardner • Leonard Gaudos • Denise Gaumer • Leonard Gaydos • Charlotte Gebhardt • Catherine Gebhart • Dale Gehring • Daniel Gerber • Nancy Gerber • LaDell Gerdes • Jonathan Gering • Tom Gerry • Dean Gesch • Wayne Gibson • Joan Giebink • John Giegling • David Gilbertson • Tricia Gillen • Adam Gillett • James Gilmore • Gina Giovannetti • Sally Goeman • Judy Goetz • Marcus Goetz • Gabriela Gomez • Kathy (Donahue) Goodale • Doug Gordon • Scott Gordon • Ken Graack • Layth Grangaard • Brian Granneman • Charlene Grant • Jay Grav • Ronald Grave • Jay Gray • Chuck Greco • Ed Green • Cheryl (Storey) Greenhagen • Dennis Greenhagen • Dave Greenlee • John Greenlee • Michael Greenlee • Sue (Jenson) Greenlee • David Gregling • Rick Gresdahl • Bonnie Griffith • Richard Grismer • Janet Gritzner • Cathy Groen • Don Grooms • Jean Gropper • Jess Grunblatt • Gretchen Gubbrud • Ardis Guildner • Faye Gunderson • Jim Gunn • Anita Gunvaldson • Kelley Gustafson • Donna (Cory) Haacke • Bob Haas • Kathleen Hackworth • Jim Haga • Jim Hagedorn • Cecilia Hagemeyer • JoAnn Hagen • Albert Hahn • Robert Haigh • Audrey Hain • Dave Hair • James Hall • Michael Hall • John Hamann • Kyle Hamann • Robert Hamann • Debora Hames • Julia Hance • Phyllis Hance • Russ Hanken • Arlen Hansen • Deanna Hansen • Greg Hansen • Larry Hansen • Linda D. Hansen • Linda K. Hansen • Traci Hansen • Walter Hansen • Arden Hanson • Bonnie Hanson • Gail (Schauneman) Hanson • Joel Hanson • Lynette Hanson • Myrna Hanson • Stan Hanson • Wayne Hanson • Bill Happel • Jean Happel • Lawrence Happel • Debbie Haraldson • Glen Harms • Marlys Harms • Deborah Harr • Melanie Harr • Emily Harrington • George Harris • Jim Harris • Kelvin Harris • Sharon Harrison • Geoffrey Hartig • David Hartzell • Joyce Hassenbroek • Dave Hastings • Jeffrey Hauck • Andrea Haugen • Chris Haugen • Connie (Feyereisen) Haugen • Leila Haugen • Harris Haupt • Eileen Hauswald • Thomas Hawkey • Carroll Hayden • Ron Hayes • Jacqueline Hazel • Nathan Headley • Marjorie Hecht • Dianna Hefte • Hazel Hegge • Kathy (Schmidt) Hegge • Kent Hegge • Dennis Heidebrink • Linda Heilman • Audrey Hein • Richard Heinemann • Dennis Helder • Steve Heller • Jim Hemmer • David Hemmingson • Jerry Hemmingson • Robin Hempel • Erick Hendrickson • Heath Henjum • Ellaine Henriksen • Nathan Henry • Al Hepner • Sue Hepner • Amy Herman • Carol Hermanson • Gary Hermanson • Robin Hermanson • Elizabeth Hertz • Roger Hessler • Dennis Hetrick • Dallas Hewett • George Hick • June (Rothberg) Hick • Robert Hider • Carolyn (Koball) Hieb • Luke Hieb • Kris Higgins • Liz Higgins • Millie Higgins • Glen Hildebrandt • Mark Hillesheim • Crain Hillestad • Arlene Hines • Frank Hines • Joe Hinricher • Steve Hitterdal • Kenneth Hitzeman • Thomas Hodges • Darrell Hodne • Doreen Hoeck • Terry Hoerner • Jeffrey Hofer • Ricky Hoff • Pat Holkenbrink • Kent Holland • Doug Hollaren • Bill Holler • Eric Holm • Tom Holm • Nancy Holt • Sheri (Gulbranson) Holt • Nancy Holzapfel • Rodney Honey • Scott Honey • Rodney Honeycutt • Dennis Hood • Joy (Peterson) Hood • Martin Hood • Jean Hook • David Hopkins • Martha Hopper • Paul Horstad • Burt Horsted • Emil Horvath • Ron Hosenfeld • Karen Houchins • Andrea Hougan • Treva Houska • Jim Hovatter • Penney Hovatter • Tanya Hovatter • Laramie Hovde • Steve Howard • Janet Howe • Kathy Hoyme • Nancy Hoyme • Barb Hubbling • Brian Huberty • Laura (Top) Huewe • Michael Huffert • Isabelle Hult • John Hunhoff • Beverly Hunstad • Todd Huntley • Duane Hurley • Terry Hurtgen • H.L. Hutcheson • John Hutchinson • Andrew Ingalls • Jack Ingwersen • Betty Irvine • David Issendorf • Robson Ivan • Jana Iverson • Jorge Izaurralde • Dave Jackson • Nancy Jackstatter • Andrew Jacobsen • Kathleen Jacobson • Matthew Jacobson • Ron Jacobson • Patricia Jaggie • Jon Jamsa • Andrew Jansma • Kathleen Janssen • Mike Jaqua • Steven Jarman • Tom Jellema • Larry Jelsma • Shannon Jelsma • Shawn Jelsma • Cheryl Jenkins • Ian Jenkins • Robert Jenneman • Karen Jennings • Daniel Jensen • Linda Jensen • Lynn Jensen • Paul Jensen • Robert Jensen • Timothy Jensen • Leslie Jerentowski • Marilyn Johannsen • Jonathan Johansen • Arlys Johnson • Bernie (Korang) Johnson • Betty Johnson • Brent Johnson • Cecil Johnson • Char Johnson • Connie (Zweep) Johnson • Craig Johnson • Dale Johnson • Doris Johnson • Gary Johnson • Gregg Johnson • Jeffery Johnson • Judy Johnson • Karla Johnson • Kenneth L. Johnson • Kenneth P. Johnson • Kim Johnson • Lisa Johnson • Lowell Johnson • LuAnn Johnson • Mark Johnson • Mary Johnson • Melissa Johnson • Michael Johnson • Patricia Johnson • Patty (Hertwig) Johnson • Paul Johnson • Rebecca Johnson • Ronald E. Johnson • Ronald L. Johnson • Scott Johnson • Sharon Johnson • Shirley Johnson • Steven A. Johnson • Steven M. Johnson • Willy Johnson • Kristian Johnstad • Dave Johnston • Valerie Johnston • Brenda Jones • Cheryl Jones • Gary Jones • Hiwatha Jones • John Jones • Cindy (Paggett) Jorgensen • D.A. Jorgenson • Carrie Jucht • Colleen Jucht • Damon Judd • Beverly Julson • Pamela Julson • Dawn Junker • Carmen Jurgensen • Cindy Jurgensen • Jack Jurgensen • Sharon Kadinger • Dwight Kahler • John Kaliszewski • Kevin Kallas • Linda Kalman • Tom Kalvelage • Ron Kanengieter • Stephen Kant • Marie Karban • Timothy Karda • Kevin Karli • Shirley Kasma • Connie Kasten • Larry Kasten • James Kauffold • Jason Kaufman • James Kaufold • Jeff Kautz • Carol Keating • Peggy Keegan • Jackie Keiner-Jones • Robyn Keizer • Diane Keleher • Bradley Kelly • Glenn Kelly • Ray Kelly • Dennis Kemp • Bill Kennedy • Patrick Kennedy • Scott Kenner • Nathan Keyman • William Kickland • Susan Kiehne • Kelly Kimball • Paul Kimpel • Jan King • Paula King • Kevin Kirchner • Jeri Kirkegaard • Kevin Kiss • Aljean Klaassen • Jacie Klaver • Robert Klaver • Lori Kleifgren • Jason Klein • Jeff Klein • Rod Klein • Ken Klenk • Elaine Kline • Kristi Kline • Ralph Klinger • Janet Klinghagen • Dawn Klosterbuer • Geneva Kluck • Kathleen Kluck • Homer Kludt • Bud Knopf • Jim Knox • Judy Knox • Janet Knudsen • Bonnie Knuteson • Dorothy Knutson • Holly Kobitter • Judy Koch • Paparo Kodali • Edgar Koens • Loren Koepsell • Brad Kontz • Robin Koopman • Audrey Kopecky • Claire Korslund • Bret Kortie • Jay Kost • William Kovalick • Jon Kragt • William Kramber • Diane (Fliear) Krell • Darin Krempges • Kim Kringen • Kevin Kroeger • Josh Kroger • Darrel Kronemann • Peggy Krull • Evan Kruse • Rodney Kruse • Da Kuang • Steve Kub • Don Kulow • Lisa Kurtz • Charles Kurzhal • Jim Lacasse • Mike LaCome • Keller Laging • Gary Lamb • Laurel (Anderson) Lamb

# What It Took

## A History of the USGS EROS Data Center

# What It Took

## A History of the USGS EROS Data Center

By Rebecca L. Johnson

The Center for Western Studies
Augustana College
1998

Published by
The Center for Western Studies
Box 727, Augustana College
Sioux Falls, South Dakota  57197

The Center for Western Studies is an archives, library, museum, publishing house, and educational agency concerned principally with collecting, preserving, and interpreting prehistoric, historic, and contemporary materials that document native and immigrant cultures of the northern prairie/plains. The Center promotes understanding of the region through exhibits, publications, art shows, conferences, and academic programs. It is committed, ultimately, to defining the contribution of the region to American civilization.

Library of Congress Cataloging-in-Publication Data:

Johnson, Rebecca L.
What It Took : A History of the USGS EROS Data Center / by Rebecca L. Johnson
        p. cm.
ISBN 0-931170-66-4
1. EROS Data Center — History.  I. EROS Data Center.  II. Title.
QE76.J64  1998                                                     98-18118
550—dc21                                                              CIP


Manufactured in the United States of America
Printed by Sioux Printing, Inc., Sioux Falls, SD

# United States Department of the Interior

GEOLOGICAL SURVEY
EROS Data Center
Sioux Falls, South Dakota 57198

Dear Friends of EROS:

*What It Took: A History of the U.S. Geological Survey's EROS Data Center* is a wonderful story about people. It all started back in the mid-1960's as only a gleam in the eyes of a few individuals within the USGS who had an extraordinary vision and then did whatever was required to fulfill that vision. A few community leaders in South Dakota embraced that same vision and then applied a level of resourcefulness, sometimes beyond belief, to do whatever was required to bring EROS to Sioux Falls.

The true EROS pioneers were the handful of folks who started the operations in rented space in the center of Sioux Falls and the larger group of 'downtowners' who, 25 years ago, moved into the new facilities northeast of the city. Following the move, more than 1800 current and former employees did whatever was required to make the EROS Data Center a world-class institution for receiving, processing, archiving, distributing, researching and applying remote sensing data taken of the Earth.

This year, 1998, is the EROS Data Center's Silver Anniversary, and this book, expertly authored by Rebecca Johnson, tops off our anniversary celebration by capturing the spirit, enthusiasm and dedication of the people who did whatever was required to make EROS a success.

We are particularly indebted to the sponsoring organizations that provided the financial resources needed to prepare and publish this book. They are:

Raytheon Corporation
Sioux Falls Development Foundation
Sioux Valley-Southwestern Electric Cooperative
East River Electric
Basin Electric Power Cooperative
Splitrock Telecom
Spitznagel, Inc.
Gil Haugan Construction
Viking Engineering Service Company

Sioux Falls Area Foundation
Norwest Bank
Sioux Falls Convention and Visitors Bureau
Schock Family Foundation
Elmen Family Foundation
Sioux Falls Chamber of Commerce
Ampex
Eastman Kodak Company
Hander Plumbing and Heating, Inc.

Finally, a special thanks goes to Russ Pohl, Al Schock, and Dave Stenseth who not only helped bring EROS to Sioux Falls, but also worked with our sponsors to secure the funds for the book — just another example of what it took.

Donald T. Lauer, Ph.D.
Chief, EROS Data Center
U.S. Geological Survey

# Acknowledgments

The task of pulling together diverse records and recollections to write this history of the EROS Data Center has been a challenging one, and one that I could not have accomplished without the assistance of many people.

I would like to thank Raytheon STX for its generous support of this project, and Dave Stenseth, Russ Pohl and Al Schock for their fund-raising efforts, without which the publishing of this book would not have been possible. Jim Sturdevant provided constant support and encouragement, and always found me a place to sit and work!

G.O. Richards, Don Becker, and Rita Tornow helped greatly in locating and identifying many of the photographs, as did Lee McManus and Jan Nelson, who also designed the cover, with assistance from Darla Larsen.

Many thanks to the individuals who reviewed drafts of the text, especially Glenn Landis and R.J. Thompson, both of whom spent much time and considerable effort helping me craft an historically accurate account of many of the events in the EDC's history. And a special 'thank you' to Rita T., who helped in countless ways that made this undertaking much easier.

Finally, and most importantly, I would like to thank all the people associated with the EROS Data Center who agreed to be interviewed and let their words become a part of this book. I sincerely appreciate their willingness to answer my questions, share memories, describe events, explain technical details, and in general, help me to understand "what it took."

Rebecca L. Johnson

# About the Author

Rebecca L. Johnson is an award-winning freelance science author who writes for both children and adults on topics ranging from environmental issues and cutting-edge scientific research to natural history. She is the author of numerous books, including *The Greenhouse Effect: Life on a Warmer Planet* (1990), *The Great Barrier Reef: A Living Laboratory* (1991), and *Investigating the Ozone Hole* (1993). Her *Science on the Ice: An Antarctic Journal* (1995) received the *Scientific American* Young Readers Book Award, the *Children's Literature* Choice List Award, and the NSTA/CBC Outstanding Science Trade Book for Children Award. Both that book, as well as her recent *Braving the Frozen Frontier: Women Working In Antarctica* (1997) are based on firsthand research in Antarctica supported by the National Science Foundation. The author has been a feature writer for The Discovery Channel Online Magazine and a frequent guest with Online Classroom. She also works with several national publishing houses as a writer, editor and consultant for grade-school, middle-school and high-school science textbooks. Johnson is a native of Sioux Falls, SD.

# Table of Contents

*The EROS Data Center stands out against the rural countryside of southeastern South Dakota.*

# – 1 –
# Lift Off!

"*T* minus 60 seconds and counting..."
The voice blares out over the loudspeaker at Mission Control at NASA's Western Test Range at Vandenberg Air Force Base in southern California. It is Sunday morning, July 23, 1972, just after 11 A.M. Dry summer winds sweep across the launch pad toward a towering Delta rocket that stands poised beneath a leaden sky of low clouds. Sitting atop the rocket is its one-ton payload, the first Earth Resources Technology Satellite, dubbed ERTS–1

*Members of the Sioux Falls delegation tour Mission Control at Vandenberg Air Force Base.*

*The Delta rocket carrying ERTS–1, just prior to lift-off*

for short, the technological heart of the U.S. Geological Survey's Earth Resources Observation Systems (EROS) Program.

Inside Mission Control, the air fairly bristles with tension. The launch has been delayed several times during the previous few days, and it is beginning to look as if the rocket might never get off the ground. Among the anxious spectators is a small group of about two dozen people from, of all places, South Dakota. They are a mix of business leaders, politicians, and government managers. They stand clustered together, hardly speaking, eyes fixed on the launch pad as if the future depends on the success or failure of this launch.

"T minus 10, 9, 8, 7, 6, 5, 4, 3...2...1...Ignition... We have lift-off!"

With flames and smoke streaming from its base, the Delta rises from the launch pad. A reverberating roar rocks the base, rattling the windows of Mission Control as the rocket climbs slowly skyward, its tail a brilliant fireball. Seconds later it disappears into the clouds. Relief floods through the crowd, amid cheers and applause. The "bird" is off and a new era in the quest to better understand the Earth and its resources has begun.

*ERTS–1 in orbit*

*The rocket rises from the launch pad and heads into space.*

\* \* \*

Five hundred miles above the Earth's surface on that hot July day in 1972, ERTS–1 settled into orbit. Its butterfly wings opened, sensors hummed to life, and the satellite began taking pictures of the planet and transmitting those images back to Earth.

The launch of ERTS–1 ushered in a new era in the field of remote sensing. Simply put, remote sensing is a way of gathering information — data — using instruments that are some distance from whatever is being studied. Perhaps the most familiar remote sensor is the camera. With a camera, you can take pictures — remotely sensed images — of the world around you. Mount a camera on an airplane, and you can get a bird's-eye-view of lakes, mountains, and urban areas. Put a camera into orbit, and your view of the Earth expands enormously.

ERTS–1 (later renamed Landsat–1) was the first remote sensing satellite launched for the specific purpose of studying Earth's natural resources. Researchers hoped to use the images beamed down from the satellite's sensors to help manage forests and grasslands, locate mineral

and oil deposits, track fires and floods, and monitor global change. Its launch signified a major advance in global environmental research.

For that small delegation from South Dakota, the launching of ERTS–1 was significant for

*Remotely sensed satellite images give a unique perspective of the Earth's surface, such as this view of Albania.*

another reason. All the images that were going to be taken by that satellite, and those planned to come after it, were destined for the EROS Data Center back home in their state. The EROS Data Center, located just outside of Sioux Falls, South Dakota, was to become the site of one of the largest collections of remotely sensed data about the Earth and its resources ever assembled.

And so it has. Today, the EROS Data Center, or simply the EDC, is one of the most extensive civilian repositories of remotely sensed data about global land resources in the world. Secure within its walls are 9 million aerial photographs and more than 3 million remotely sensed satellite images of the Earth's land surface.

As one of five field centers operated by the National Mapping Division of the U.S. Geological Survey, an agency of the Department of the Interior (DOI), the EROS Data Center is involved in receiving, archiving, researching and

distributing remotely sensed data. In addition to its extensive remotely sensed data archive, the EDC also maintains and distributes digital cartographic data of the nation. This invaluable and ever-expanding storehouse of information about the Earth's land surfaces is used by EDC scientists, as well as researchers in private industry, at colleges and universities, and at government institutions in dozens of countries, to better understand the planet's resources and how Earth has changed over time.

The EDC has changed, too. It has evolved from a handful of people housed in temporary quarters to a world-class data analysis and research laboratory. The story of that transformation is one of vision and hope, of formidable problems and creative solutions, and of determination, hard work, and a "can-do" spirit that has become the hallmark of the EROS Data Center throughout its history.

*The USGS EROS Data Center today*

# – 2 –
# Beginnings

The EROS Data Center, the EROS Program, and the ERTS–1 satellite can all trace their roots back to the earliest days of remote sensing, when the camera was invented in the 1800s. Here was a new tool that allowed people to record the world around them in a versatile way. Eager to gain unique perspectives on that world, photographers clambered up mountains, perched on tall buildings, and went aloft in balloons.

With the coming of the airplane at the end of the 19th century, the fledgling field of remote sensing literally took flight. Airplanes carried photographers and their cameras to heights and places that were previously out of reach. Photographs taken thousands of feet above the Earth's surface revealed more about its geography, geology, and natural resources than had ever before been possible.

Military strategists used aerial photography extensively in both World War I and II. Between the wars, a civilian aerial photography industry sprang up that used aerial photographs for mineral exploration, crop analyses and timber surveys, and for making detailed maps.

Following World War II, cameras were improved and new types of film were developed, including color infrared film that recorded images produced by reflected infrared energy — energy from the Sun that is invisible to the human eye, but highly reflected by green plants. Other types of non-photographic sensors, such as thermal-infrared sensors and radar, were also added to a growing list of remote sensing devices.

The field of remote sensing took a huge leap forward with the coming of the Space Age in the late 1950s. In 1957, the Soviets launched *Sputnik,* the first artificial Earth-orbiting satellite, and the space race between the United States and the U.S.S.R. began in earnest. In 1958, the National

*Balloons were among the earliest high-altitude platforms used to photograph the Earth's surface.*

Aeronautics and Space Administration, or NASA, was created, and soon afterwards charged by President John F. Kennedy with the task of landing a manned spacecraft on the Moon by the end of the 1960s.

It was a daunting proposition. Not the least of the challenges was how to gather information about the nature of the lunar surface prior to actually landing there. Researchers at NASA, as well as teams of scientists from several universities and other federal agencies, including the U.S. Geological Survey, worked to design new types of sensors for scanning the Moon's surface.

Along with those sensors, new ways of interpreting and using remotely sensed data also needed to be developed.

The most expedient way to try out the new sensors that resulted from these efforts was to fly them over terrestrial test sites, and analyze the results. It was during these test flights that researchers realized that the sensors which had been created to explore the Moon and outer space also had enormous potential for investigating the Earth. Here was a novel way to view the planet, with a truly global perspective. The results of these test flights, and their implications for viewing the Earth from space, sparked great enthusiasm among the research teams. So did data collected from weather satellites equipped with remote sensors, and startling pictures of the planet taken by *Mercury* and *Gemini* astronauts using hand-held cameras during the early 1960s.

Nowhere was enthusiasm greater than at the Department of the Interior, and especially in the U.S. Geological Survey. USGS scientists had a continuing need for huge amounts of data about the geography, geology, hydrology, and natural resources of the nation's land surfaces in order to carry out their research and to make accurate maps. Long-distance, synoptic views of the Earth would be invaluable to the DOI in fulfilling its mission. Encouraged by the progress being made in remote sensing technology — and realizing how views of Earth from space could help them in their work — USGS scientists began urging NASA to move ahead as quickly as possible with plans to develop an

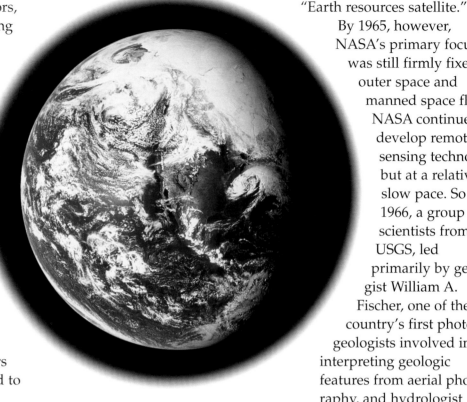

*A view of Earth — the Blue Planet — from space*

"Earth resources satellite." By 1965, however, NASA's primary focus was still firmly fixed on outer space and manned space flight. NASA continued to develop remote sensing technology, but at a relatively slow pace. So in 1966, a group of scientists from the USGS, led primarily by geologist William A. Fischer, one of the country's first photogeologists involved in interpreting geologic features from aerial photography, and hydrologist Charles J. Robinove, grew impatient with the situation. Strong advocates of remote sensing from space, Fischer and Robinove were convinced that the current sensors were good enough, at least initially, to do the job. It was time for action.

*"Bill was so enthusiastic about [remote sensing from space]. He felt if they could put a man on the Moon, they should be able to find from space diseased crops, and schools of fish, and new sources of oil, and all sorts of other things."*

— Blanche Fischer, widow of William Fischer

*"Bill Fischer's early pioneer work in photogeology and remote sensing laid the groundwork for the formulation, development and consummation of the EROS program. Bill was 'Mr. EROS'."*

— Sue Sousa, former technical assistant to William Fischer, and Exhibits and Information Officer, EROS Program

*William A. Fischer, one of the EROS Program's earliest and strongest supporters*

The two scientists went to see William T. Pecora, who was director of the USGS at the time (and would later become Undersecretary of the Department of the Interior). Fischer and Robinove presented their case for immediate action on remote sensing of the Earth from space, and put forth the suggestion that perhaps the DOI should develop its own satellite program. Pecora liked the idea, and felt the program would be good for the country.

Pecora, Fischer and Robinove then presented the proposal for a remote sensing satellite program to the Secretary of the Interior, Stewart L. Udall. Udall, being a strong advocate for the environment, was soon convinced as well. A plan was prepared in secret, and on September 21, 1966, Udall announced at a press conference — and no doubt shocked most members of the remote sensing community — that the DOI was launching a new endeavor called Project EROS. The acronym stood for Earth Resources Observation Satellites, and the goal of the project was to gather facts about the natural resources of the planet using Earth-orbiting satellites that carried sophisticated remote sensing instruments.

Project EROS would be under the control of the Earth Resources Observation Systems Program, a Department of the Interior effort managed directly by the U.S. Geological Survey. Udall named William Pecora to head the EROS Program, while Fischer became its research coordinator.

*"...the time is now right and urgent to apply space technology towards the solution of many pressing natural resource problems being compounded by population and industrial growth."*
— Stewart L. Udall (1966), from his speech announcing Project EROS

In speaking to the press following Udall's announcement, Pecora said that he visualized EROS "as an evolutionary program, beginning with television cameras flown in an orbit that will cover the entire surface of the Earth repeatedly, under near-identical conditions of illumination." He explained that the DOI planned to fly their first satellite, estimated to cost $20 million, just three years later, in 1969!

*"The course seems clear; we must make and execute bold plans to gather data on the Earth's resources.... Project EROS is dedicated to this task.... We now stand ready to start the EROS Program...and to accelerate the search for natural resources."*
— William T. Pecora (1966)

*William T. Pecora (right), being interviewed about the EROS Program*

However, neither the USGS nor the DOI had the resources available to fund their own satellite program at this time. By some accounts, Udall's announcement creating the EROS Program that September day in 1966 was largely a political move designed to motivate NASA to hurry along with the remote sensing program. It also had the effect of skirting objections raised by the Department of Defense about establishing a satellite program that would not be under military control.

*"Pecora, Fischer, and Robinove felt that we ought to be devoting more attention to looking at the Earth than outer space. So they convinced Udall to basically twist NASA's arm [with the announcement]. It was a total bluff. But it worked!"*
— Glenn Landis, first Chief of the EROS Data Center

*"The problem was with the Department of Defense, which already had satellites that were far superior to ERTS. So did the Soviets, but the DOD's concern was that smaller countries didn't, and this new system might give those countries an edge.... The real goal was to get a satellite, to get something working, and then refine it from there. But the first step was to get around the Defense Department's objections to any satellite."*
— William Pecora, Jr., son of William T. Pecora

By 1968, NASA was poised to begin building the first ERTS satellite, which it planned to launch in late 1971 or early 1972. Within the Department of the Interior, EROS Program

personnel turned their attention to another aspect of the project: the handling and distribution of the data the satellite would produce.

During its first year of operation, ERTS–1 would be snapping 25,000 or more digital pictures of the planet, and beaming them back to Earth. Who would handle and distribute all the data that the satellite — and those planned to follow it — would generate? NASA wasn't interested in managing millions of satellite images. But the DOI, on the other hand, jumped at the opportunity.

Building a major data distribution center for the EROS Program quickly became a top priority at the USGS. The agency contracted RCA's Astro Electronics Division to do a "Ground Data-Handling System Study" for the ERTS system. RCA's report proposed a plan for such a center, and recommended that it be located where it could receive transmissions directly from satellites passing over any part of the continental United States. This limited the possible sites for an "EROS Data Center" to an elliptical zone about 350 miles long and 150 miles wide in the center of the country, a zone that stretched from Topeka, Kansas, to just north of Sioux Falls, South Dakota.

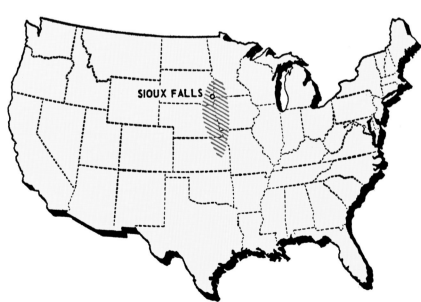

*The ideal location for the proposed EROS data distribution center (shaded area) was in the middle of the continental United States.*

# – 3 –
# The South Dakota Connection

W ord of the USGS plan for a satellite data distribution center — and the fact that it had to be located somewhere in the central United States — soon reached the ears of two influential South Dakota politicians, Republican Senator Karl E. Mundt and Republican Congressman Ben Reifel.

*Senator Karl E. Mundt (1900 – 1974)*

Mundt, a senior senator who had begun his congressional career in 1938, wielded considerable power in the Senate. At the time, he was ranking Republican on the Senate Interior Appropriations Committee, and a very close friend of newly elected President Richard M. Nixon. Mundt and Nixon had served together in the Senate. It was said that Mundt met with Nixon every Monday morning.

Mundt saw a tremendous opportunity for his home state in the EROS Data Center. The specifications for the site fit Sioux Falls, the state's

largest city. Apart from the national publicity that the EDC would generate, Mundt envisioned that its coming to South Dakota would advance economic development and bring "space-age" technology and technological jobs to the state.

*"He [Mundt] was a power, he got the thing going."*
— Walter Conahan, Sen. Karl Mundt's former press secretary, from a 1989 *Argus Leader* interview

Congressman Ben Reifel was the ranking Republican member of the House Interior Appropriations Committee. Like Mundt, Reifel

*Close friends and colleagues, Senator Mundt and President Nixon pose for a photograph in the late 1960s.*

*Russ Pohl (left) and Dave Stenseth (right) discuss the EROS Program with North Dakota Senator Milton Young.*

was keen to see South Dakota land the prize of the EROS Data Center.

Another advocate for South Dakota in the EDC site selection process was Merlyn Veren. A South Dakota native, Veren was a lobbyist, employed by the South Dakota Board of Regents and the state's Industrial Development Agency in Washington. Part of his job was to obtain surplus government property for South Dakota universities. Veren shuttled back and forth between South Dakota and the nation's capital, and kept in close contact with Mundt and Reifel. When he heard about the EDC project, he quickly became an active proponent.

Mundt, Reifel and Veren discretely relayed their knowledge about the project to local leaders in the Sioux Falls area, and urged them to begin promoting the city as an ideal location for the satellite data center. In early 1969, Veren met with a number of business and community leaders from the Sioux Falls region, including Al Schock, president of Nordica International (and soon-to-be president of the Sioux Falls Development Foundation), Russ Pohl, vice president of Raven Industries, which manufactured high-altitude research balloons, and Dave Stenseth, Director of Development at Augustana College (and soon-to-be executive vice president of the

Development Foundation). Stenseth, especially, had numerous contacts in Washington, D.C., and "on the Hill." Veren enlisted the support of these men, along with many others in the community and the state, in working to snare the Data Center for Sioux Falls. At the Development Foundation, an "EROS committee" was formed, with Russ Pohl as chairman.

> *"We met with Veren, who said they were going to put up an Earth-orbiting satellite to monitor the Earth...called ERTS.... But he stressed we were going to have to really compete for this if we wanted to get it for Sioux Falls."*
>
> — Russ Pohl

With input from Development Foundation members, Pohl put together a proposal to the USGS that delineated why Sioux Falls was the perfect site for the new satellite data processing facility. In the months that followed, the courtship of EROS Program officials intensified. Veren and a South Dakota delegation comprised of Foundation members and local community leaders made dozens of trips to Washington to discuss the project with Mundt and Reifel, as well as with William Pecora and others at the USGS and the DOI.

In the meantime, budget wars were raging between the Bureau of the Budget (later called the Office of Management and Budget) and the two primary agencies involved with the EROS Program, NASA and the USGS. Funding for both the ERTS satellite and the EROS data processing center was repeatedly under fire, primarily from supporters of the nation's defense intelligence community. During the summer of 1969, Mundt and Reifel, in their respective positions in the Senate and House Interior Appropriations Committees, proposed amendments to restore some of the EROS Program's lost funding, including $300,000 designated for the planning of the data center facility. In September, 1969, restoration of the funding was approved by the Senate committee. In an interview following that announcement, Mundt commented that he had "received a definite promise from the operation agency destined to handle this large new data and receiving center that Sioux Falls will be among the cities personally visited and evaluated by the site selection panel." Mundt had successfully exerted his political clout, and Sioux Falls was now officially in the running.

*Al Schock (left) with Sioux Falls Mayor Mike Schirmer*

Close on the heels of this success, however, the senator suffered a totally debilitating stroke in November, 1969. Mundt remained in office, but the responsibility for continuing the quest for the EDC was shouldered by members of his staff, particularly his administrative assistant, Bob McCaughey. A number of Mundt's congressional colleagues also came to his — and South Dakota's — aid as a result of this unfortunate turn of events. Senator Milton Young of North Dakota was one of those strong supporters. A close friend of Mundt's, Young became an advocate for locating the EDC in Sioux Falls when Mundt fell ill.

Mundt's untimely illness was a set-back, especially when the Bureau of the Budget subsequently refused to release the $300,000 necessary to continue with the site selection process. Additional persuasive measures were needed to keep the EDC project, and the process of securing it, from stalling. In early 1970, Veren arranged for a delegation that included Al Schock, Russ Pohl, and Sioux Falls mayor Mike Schirmer, along with Bob McCaughey and a representative from Ben Reifel's office, to meet with James Schlesinger, then director of the Bureau of the Budget. The purpose of the meeting was first, to enlist Schlesinger's support for locating the EDC in Sioux Falls, and second, to secure the release of the $300,000 in appropriations. Schock was selected to give the sales pitch. When he finished, he was stunned when Schlesinger eyed him coldly and asked (as if Schock's words had made no impression whatsoever): "Why Sioux Falls?"

Caught off guard, Schock said the first thing that popped into his head — that Sioux Falls would donate the land on which to build the center.

*"I'd just given my pitch, so I searched my mind and said, 'Well, we'll give the land.' I thought it would be about 10 acres. Later, when we were told 320 acres, I said, 'Whatever is required, we will do it.' And that became our slogan and motto."*

— Al Schock

**Weather**

Sioux Falls Area: Chance of occasional light snow early Tuesday night. Low near 12 Tuesday night. Colder Wednesday with a high near 30. See Weather Scope, page 2.

# Sioux Falls
# ARGUS-LEADER
A Newspaper for the Home

**In Today's Paper**

| | |
|---|---|
| Editorials | 4 |
| Heloise | 6 |
| Billy Graham | 15 |
| Ann Landers | 12 |
| Markets | 16 |

| | |
|---|---|
| Round Robin | 3 |
| Sports | 13, 14 |
| TV, Movies | 11 |
| Dr. Van Dellen | 12 |
| Women | 5 |

20 PAGES ★★★ DAILY AND SUNDAY  SIOUX FALLS, SOUTH DAKOTA  TUESDAY, MARCH 31, 1970  TELEPHONE 336-1130  10 CENTS

*Mundt's Office Announces White House Decision*

## Sioux Falls To Be Site Of Satellite Data Center

*The selection of Sioux Falls as the site for the EROS Data Center was front-page news on March 31, 1970.*

U.S. Sen. Karl Mundt's office announced in Washington late Monday that Sioux Falls has been chosen as the location for an international data reception center for the federal government's earth resources program if experimental satellites prove successful.

which data is collected from the earth's surface through devices such as cameras.

He said information collected by the satellite remote sensing equipment must be transmitted to a ground station for processing and dissemination.

This ground station, or data reception center

for "Earth Resources Technology Satellite," he said, and will precede another launching in 1973 of a similar satellite which will be called ERTS-B.

McCaughey said NASA officials confirmed late in February that the satellite launching schedules were considered "reasonably firm"

the first year of operation, Mundt's aide said, the center is expected to employ 150 persons with an annual payroll of $1.8 million. Most of the personnel will be individuals with scientific and technical backgrounds.

McCaughey said the first operational year of ERTS-A is

tem and potential sites, indicates that after about two years of operation about 1.5 million prints, both color and black-and-white, will be needed each year to supply public demand for resources information.

Mundt's assistant said the data center would be expected to attract

---

The offer of free land certainly sweetened the pie. As Dave Stenseth put it: "People in Washington and in Sioux Falls finally began to believe that Sioux Falls was indeed the home for EROS. All the talk, all the trips to Washington...all of the promises began to take hold. Sioux Falls was viable! Sioux Falls was attractive...! But Sioux Falls also had, or would have, that promised free land...."

Yet the federal funds that had been appropriated for site selection and facility planning were still not forthcoming. In early March, 1970, a letter to Nixon went out of Mundt's office, bearing the senator's signature, appealing to the President to name Sioux Falls as the data center site, and to release the necessary funds to move ahead with the project.

*"So Mundt wrote, or...signed, this 'Dear Dick' letter — 'One thing left in my political career...it would be nice to see this project come to the state...' — and so on. I mean, it was almost tear-stained. And it worked PRETTY WELL!"*

— Dave Stenseth

The letter had the desired effect. On March 30, 1970, Mundt's office issued a press release announcing that Sioux Falls had been named as the site for the EDC.

Years later, Bob McCaughey admitted there had been a little more to the story, however. After the letter of appeal had been sent to Nixon, McCaughey went to see White House Chief of Staff Bryce Harlow to discuss the EROS project and Sioux Falls' chances for being selected. Harlow later called McCaughey and told him that it looked like South Dakota would be selected. In composing the press release that went out on March 30, McCaughey chose to leave out the phrase "looked like" and stated simply that Sioux Falls had been chosen. The release was sent in the afternoon, with a copy going out the following day to Harlow. Upon seeing the release — which by then had been run in every newspaper in South Dakota — the Chief of Staff called McCaughey back and said, "You got the White House looking quite a bit pregnant [with this announcement]. We are going through with it — it's going to get done."

The White House did carry through on its promise, and Sioux Falls, South Dakota became the official site of the EROS Data Center. A great deal of time, effort, and political favors had been spent securing the Center for Sioux Falls. The challenge ahead was equally formidable: raising the money necessary to buy the land on which the EDC would eventually be located. But as Al Schock was so often heard to say, "Whatever is required, we will do it."

# – 4 –
# Operation Ground Shot

*I*n many respects, the EROS Data Center project was perfectly timed for the city of Sioux Falls, and for those who were interested in seeing it develop economically. For some time, the Sioux Falls Development Foundation, the Chamber of Commerce (headed by Louis Warren at the time) and many members of the city's business community had been hoping to buy land north of the city to create an Industrial Park that they believed would act as a drawing card to attract new industry to the city. Now, with the prospect of Sioux Falls becoming the site of a high-tech satellite data processing lab, community leaders saw an opportunity to achieve two goals at the same time.

Efforts to raise awareness, excitement, and eventually money to purchase land for the Data Center — and the Industrial Park — began in April, 1970, with "Industrial Development Week," an unprecedented effort to promote the city's industrial growth. In Mayor Mike Schirmer's words, the whole purpose of Industrial Development Week was "to acquaint all people in Sioux Falls with the job that's to be done." For a two-dollar donation to the Development Foundation, local citizens received membership cards and buttons proclaiming them "Sioux Empire Builders." One of the special attractions during

Industrial Development Week was a traveling display featuring exhibits from local industries, a photo display about the EROS Program, samples of Moon dust and a miniature South Dakota flag that had been to the Moon and back, courtesy of the *Apollo 11* astronauts.

Industrial Development Week was launched with a kick-off luncheon on April 23, 1970. William Pecora, head of the EROS Program Office in Washington, D.C. and Director of the USGS, was invited as the keynote speaker. When Pecora, accompanied by Congressman Ben

*An advertisement in the Sioux Falls* **Argus Leader** *announces Industrial Development Week and encourages citizens to become "Sioux Empire Builders."*

*Mayor Mike Schirmer signs the document proclaiming April 23-30, 1970, as Industrial Development Week, as Bob Elmen (left), chairman of ID Week activities, and Dave Stenseth (right) look on.*

Reifel, arrived at the airport, it was raining and threatening snow. But the weather didn't dampen the welcome he received. A red carpet was unfurled as he stepped down from the plane and was met by an enthusiastic group of

Development Foundation members, city officials and members of the press.

At the luncheon, where the motto was "First the Moon, Now the Earth," Pecora spoke about the benefits of the EROS Program to the United States and the world. He described how the ERTS–1 satellite would collect information about various aspects of the Earth, including agriculture, forests and mineral deposits, and would feed that information directly to the Data Center.

Pecora outlined the job that was facing the city at this point. A building site would have to be selected in the area that fulfilled the long list of requirements set forth by the RCA study. The site needed to be 100 acres in size, surrounded by a 200-acre buffer zone. The ideal location would be roughly ten miles from the Sioux Falls airport, in an area with stable soil that could support large antennas, an ample water supply for photo processing, and relatively little radio frequency interference or other electronic "noise." The $300,000 which Mundt and Reifel had secured in appropriations — but which Pecora noted had yet to be released by the

*William Pecora shakes hands with Al Schock after arriving in Sioux Falls for the beginning of Industrial Development Week. (Front, left to right: Al Schock, Mike Schirmer, Congressman Ben Reifel, William Pecora. Back, left to right: Bob Elmen, Louis Warren, unknown, Dave Stenseth, Merlyn Veren)*

*The cover of the Operation Ground Shot brochure, produced by the Development Foundation*

Bureau of the Budget — was to be used for site selection and testing.

Pecora's visit created considerable excitement. The benefits of the EROS Program to humankind were expounded at great length, as were the more immediate benefits to the city of Sioux Falls and the surrounding area. Initially, it was thought the Center would employ about 150 people. But caught up, perhaps, in the enthusiasm of the moment, more extravagant claims were made in the coming months, some to the effect that within 5 or 10 years, the EROS Data Center would have a workforce of 4,500 to 5,000!

Industrial Development Week set the stage for the next step in establishing the Data Center: Operation Ground Shot. This was a fund drive, organized by the Development Foundation, in which raising money for the EROS land deal was linked with the acquisition of land for an Industrial Park. The goal of Operation Ground Shot was to raise $390,000 in a relatively short period of time. Of that amount, $150,000 would go to purchase the land for the Data Center site. The remaining $240,000 would be used to purchase and develop the land targeted for an Industrial Park. The slogan for the fund drive, emblazoned on the brochure produced by the Foundation and complete with an artist's vision of what the Data Center might look like, was "A Small Goal for a Multi-Million Dollar Future."

Operation Ground Shot was launched on May 21, 1970. Forty-five teams of two men each were organized by the Development Foundation to go out into the business community and solicit donations for the cause. At the end of the first official day of fund-raising, $150,000 had been pledged to Operation Ground Shot. Less than a week later that amount had risen to $275,000. The goal of $390,000 was reached within one month, and when the drive was completed at the end of July, roughly $480,000 had been pledged.

Once Operation Ground Shot was well under

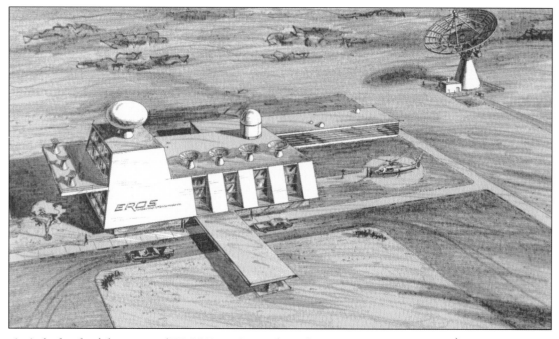

*Artist's sketch of the proposed EROS Data Center, from the Operation Ground Shot brochure*

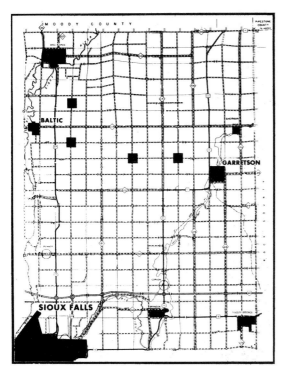

*Map showing the six initial sites chosen as possible locations for the EDC*

No one wanted to jeopardize the project at this point. So when the chief engineer of the Stanford Institute testing team told Dave Stenseth one Sunday afternoon that he wanted to climb the tower of a local television station, Stenseth called up the station's vice president and made arrangements for the engineer to get a unique view of the prairie.

*"One Sunday he said, 'Dave, you know what I'd really like to do? I'd like to climb the KELO tower. I'm a rock climber and it's the highest thing around and I'd really like to do that.' So I called up Evans Nord [vice president of KELO-TV], Sunday afternoon at home, and said, 'Evans, this may sound strange, but I've got this guy from Stanford on this EROS deal, and he wants to climb your tower.' I told him about the engineer's request, and said he'd sign a release. So the guy went and climbed the tower. We stood on the ground, watching him, and he was very happy when he came down."*

— Dave Stenseth

way, a team consisting of Schock, Stenseth, Foundation member Tom M. Reardon, realtors Joe Griffin and Tom Costello, Raven Industries president Ed Owen, and Duane Paulson, from Spitznagel Partners, Inc. architectural and engineering firm, began searching the countryside for potential sites for the EROS Data Center near Sioux Falls. By mid-June, they had identified six possible locations. Four of those were in Minnehaha County, north and east of the city, while two were in Turner County. The realtors in the group, with the advice of attorney Russell Greenfield, legal counsel for the Development Foundation, obtained land purchase options for these parcels.

Not long afterwards, a team of researchers from the Stanford Research Institute in Menlo Park, California, arrived in Sioux Falls, loaded with "sensitive electronic gear" in a specially equipped Greyhound bus. Their job was to make soil, water and radio frequency surveys of the sites. The results would be used in making the final site selection.

During the month-long testing process, local people involved with the EROS project tried to accommodate the visitors in every possible way.

On June 21, the number of sites being considered was narrowed to three, all lying between the small towns of Baltic and Garretson north of Sioux Falls. A 60-foot open metal tower was erected near these sites for the purpose of doing a "radio frequency environmental survey" to assess the electronic noise and radio interference conditions in the area.

Back in Washington, William Pecora had assembled a committee to evaluate the three sites. In late July, committee members flew in to visit the sites and review the test results, and on August 13, 1970, the choice was made. The EROS Data Center was to be located on the middle site, 12 miles north and 4 miles east of Sioux Falls, on 318 acres of farmland near the small town of Garretson. The land belonged to two long-time farming families, Rudolph and Olga Froseth and Alfred and Annettie Hegge.

Both couples had owned and farmed their land for many years. The Froseths were quite happy to sell their land since they were planning to retire from farming within a year or two. The

*The 60-foot "testing tower" erected by the Stanford Research Institute between Baltic and Garretson*

Hegges, however, were reluctant to leave. Alfred Hegge's father had homesteaded their quarter section nearly 100 years earlier, in 1873, and it had been in the family ever since. But after considerable negotiations, the Hegges, too, agreed to sell.

> *"You have a lot of memories after 81 years in one home, and we certainly will have some regrets at leaving."*
>
> — Alfred Hegge (1970),
> after his farm was selected
> as the site of the EDC

> *"There was some antigovernment sentiment when the EROS people first arrived and pushed their weight around. But everybody was excited, too, because this was the outside world coming to us. Rural South Dakota was very secluded at that time."*
>
> — Kent Hegge, great nephew of
> Alfred and Annettie Hegge

But there were still obstacles to be overcome. Earlier in the year, Pecora and others at the USGS had conveyed the news that no money had been budgeted for the actual construction of a building on the site. It seemed that extraordinary measures would be needed if all the work that had so far been done on the EROS Data Center project was to come to fruition. Once again, civic leaders and members of the Development Foundation found themselves challenged to act creatively to do "whatever was required." And their plan was a bold one: the Foundation would borrow the money necessary for construction, build the facility, and then lease it back to the federal government.

With the options to buy the Froseth and Hegge land firmly in hand, on August 14, 1970, the Foundation formally offered to donate the site to the federal government. Furthermore, they agreed to construct the EROS Data Center facility under a 20-year lease/purchase agreement, with the understanding that at the end of that time, ownership of the building would revert to the government.

A small glitch in the deal came to light concerning the land, however, when Stenseth and Development Foundation attorney Green-

*Alfred and Annettie Hegge (seated) affix their signatures to the land purchase agreement for their farm. (Back row, left to right: Claude Hamilton, Clifford Hegge, Dave Stenseth, Joe Griffin)*

*Rudolph Froseth (seated) signs documents authorizing the sale of the Froseth farm while his wife Olga and realtor Joe Griffin look on.*

field learned that the St. Paul's Norwegian Evangelical Lutheran Church had once stood on the southwest corner of the 318-acre site, across the road from the small cemetery that still lies near the entrance to the Data Center's grounds. The building itself was long gone, but the single acre of land on which it had once stood still belonged to the church as such, even though the congregation had disbanded in 1965.

Stenseth and Greenfield combed through records and made inquiries. After an extensive search, they discovered that the secretary of the former congregation was living in

*St. Paul's Evangelical Lutheran Church, as it looked in 1923*

the nearby town of Dell Rapids. They called on her, explained the situation, and after considerable discussion, convinced her that she could, and should, sell the land.

*"I worked harder on that one acre than we did on the rest of it!"*

— Dave Stenseth

After acquiring and paying for all the land needed for the Data Center, the Development Foundation decided that it would be fitting to personally deliver the deeds for the entire parcel to President Nixon at the White House. A delegation led by Governor Frank Farrar flew to Washington, and on October 26, 1970, they were ushered into the Oval Office. Within minutes, Nixon came striding in, and in front of a group of reporters and photographers, Governor Farrar presented the deeds for the land for the EROS

Data Center to the President. Nixon accepted the documents on behalf of the federal government, and subsequently authorized the spending of the $300,000 that had been appropriated more than a year earlier.

In less than six months after Sioux Falls was selected as the site for the EROS Data Center, the Development Foundation and the Sioux Falls area community had accomplished a remarkable feat. They had raised nearly a half million dollars and acquired an ideal site outside the city. As a bonus, the long-awaited Industrial Park had also been secured. Much work remained, but the EROS Data Center was well on its way to becoming a reality.

*"EROS, and the Industrial Park, changed the course of Sioux Falls. It put Sioux Falls on the map."*

— Russ Pohl

*South Dakota Governor Frank Farrar presents the deeds for the land on which the EROS Data Center will be built to President Richard M. Nixon. (Left to right: Al Schock, President Nixon, Governor Farrar, Bob McCaughey)*

# – 5 –
# Designing a Data Center

Once the site had been chosen and land acquired, USGS and EROS Program officials in Washington turned their attention to designing the EROS Data Center. The person they chose to undertake that challenge was Glenn Landis. Landis had been involved in remote sensing, primarily the interpretation of remotely sensed data, for many years in the private sector. But as the remote sensing community was a rather small one, he knew Bill Fischer and others in the Topographic Division (later called the National Mapping Division) of USGS quite well.

In December, 1970, Landis joined the Topographic Division as a research scientist. After less than a month in his new position, he was offered the job of heading up the small group that would create the Center from the ground up. Landis accepted, and plunged into the task ahead.

A satellite data processing center was something totally new. There was no precedent for such a facility, no pattern to follow. Designing the Center meant formulating a clear plan to anticipate what types of products and images customers would request, how many images its photographic laboratories would potentially produce each month and year, how the Center would communicate with its customers, whether a computer data base was needed, and what sorts of information would be best for it to contain. The list of questions to be answered, and problems to be addressed, was an extensive one.

Furthermore, early in the planning process, the decision was made that the new Center would also become the home for some 5 million frames of aerial photography, accumulated since the 1940s by the Topographic Division. That film was used to make maps of the country and was scattered among the Division's Mapping Centers. Landis saw an opportunity to broaden the archival holdings of the Center, and at the same time, relieve the Mapping Centers of an unwanted burden.

*"None of us knew for sure what an Earth Resources Observation Systems Data Center should look like, let alone how to put one together.... The 'paper was truly blank!'"*

— Glenn Landis

Yet with the ERTS–1 launch just 18 months away, the pressure was on Landis to put together this new facility in a very short time, and insure that it was ready

*Glenn Landis, first Chief of the EROS Data Center*

to begin supplying tens of thousands of photographs and other satellite data products to a diverse community of users even before the satellite headed into orbit. With the clock ticking, Landis assembled a small team of experts from various branches of the USGS to help him define the parameters of the EDC. Jim McCord came to Sioux Falls to assist with the design of the Photo Lab, which had the potential to be the government's largest and most complex civilian photo processing facility. Don Carney and Bill Kosco also joined the fledgling EDC staff and began the task of defining its scope, acquiring equipment, and outlining operating procedures.

Landis and his team immediately recognized that the new building which would eventually house the Center would never be completed in time for the launch of ERTS–1. Some sort of interim facility needed to be established while the permanent facility was being built. In early 1971, Landis found himself with a very full plate. He and his small staff needed to put together an operation that would receive, process and distribute huge numbers of remotely sensed images, search for temporary quarters in Sioux Falls, and design the building that would permanently house the Center — all at the same time.

When it came to planning the new EROS Data Center building, however, they had considerable, and expert, assistance. USGS Director William Pecora requested that his Special Assistant, William A. Schmidt, oversee the design and construction of the new facility. Schmidt was the former Administrator of Public Buildings in the General Services Administration, in essence the overseer of all the nation's federal buildings. He had most recently been involved with the construction of the Kennedy Center in Washington, D.C. In early March, 1971, the USGS also commissioned two architectural and engineering firms from Sioux Falls — Spitznagel Partners, Inc. and Fritzel, Kroeger, Griffin, and Berg — to collaborate on the design and draw up plans for the building's construction.

Over the next few months, the design team met repeatedly to hammer out the details of the complex facility. In addition to the specifics for its operation, the designers wanted the building

to be readily expandable, to blend in with its prairie setting, and to be environmentally friendly. Photo processing, especially on the scale that the Center would be undertaking, generates considerable chemical pollution. It was necessary for the building to be equipped with its own on-site waste treatment plant that incorporated a chain of aeration, sedimentation and evaporation ponds to purify the wastewater that would be produced by the Photo Lab.

Keeping electronic "noise" to a minimum was also a top priority. The site had been specifically chosen for its electronically quiet characteristics, and in order to preserve that attribute, the designers proposed changing the zoning regulations to create a five-mile buffer zone around the new building to avoid electronic interference. Of course, the concern about such interference stemmed from the assumption that antennas would be installed at the Center to receive data directly from the ERTS satellites.

The proposed restrictions within the buffer zone were rigorous: no industrial complexes or housing developments would be allowed, and no radio or television towers could be built. Power lines would need to be buried, neon signs would be banned, and all electrical equipment — from power tools to farmers' tractors — would conceivably have to be outfitted with static suppressors. Responding to the design team's request for a buffer zone around the EDC site, the Minnehaha County Planning Commission announced it would hold hearings regarding these proposed zoning changes.

*"I remember specifically hearing about the restrictions.... They came in and said we couldn't build tall buildings or silos without approval. They said that even our little tractors had to have suppressors on them so we wouldn't screw things up for the transmissions. But people don't like to be told what to do...."*

— Kent Hegge

But all the talk of zoning changes and building restrictions didn't sit well with the locals. Rural folk of independent stock, the people who lived around the site bristled at the idea that state or federal governments could control the details of their daily lives. Furthermore, many local residents were becoming increasingly suspicious of the Data Center project and the people associated with it. Rumors were flying; there was talk that the electromagnetic emissions from the satellites would lower milk production of dairy cows, that the site would be a prime target for Soviet nuclear warheads, and that chemical pollutants released from the Photo Lab would contaminate the soil and groundwater. The biggest concern, however, was that the Center's presence would drive down land prices.

*"People were worried because the Cold War was on, and they...assumed that if the Soviets bombed us, EROS would be a target. Nobody really knew what the satellites were all about."*
— Kent Hegge

The simmering tension between local residents and EROS representatives finally erupted on the sultry summer night of August 16, 1971, when the County Commission held a public hearing to discuss the plans to create a buffer zone around the EDC site. More than 300 people attended, mostly farmers and land owners who lived in the area, and whose lives, and livelihoods, would be directly impacted by the Commission's decision.

*"You could hardly get upstairs because the courthouse was full of farmers, along the stairwells, all the way up!"*
— Al Schock

Distrust and anger showed on many faces that evening in the standing-room-only crowd that packed the meeting room on the second floor of the Minnehaha County Courthouse in Sioux Falls. Some of those in attendance carried placards in protest with slogans like "Who said this is a free country?" "Police State with EROS?" and "We're Schocked, Al!"

*Members of the Minnehaha County Planning Commission discuss possible zoning changes around the EDC site.*

*An angry audience faces county commissioners and EROS Program representatives during the August, 1971, meeting about the proposed buffer zone around the EDC site.*

Glenn Landis and Bill Schmidt sat at the front table with the county commissioners, along with several representatives from the Development Foundation. The moment the meeting began, angry allegations erupted from members of the audience. In Landis' words, "All hell broke loose."

A major concern was the claim that all farm equipment would have to be fitted out with static suppressors. Landis explained that if the devices were needed, the government would supply and maintain them at no cost. Other members of the audience expressed their fears that land prices would plummet. Some objected to the manner in which the rezoning had been proposed, and there was even one alarmed spectator who was worried that the satellite transmissions would interfere with his television reception.

One by one, however, the various concerns and fears were addressed by those at the head table, and, for the most part, put to rest. The placards came down, and the crowd quietly dispersed. The following week, the commissioners approved the zoning changes without further protest from area residents.

*Placards displayed — and ultimately discarded — at the buffer zone meeting.*

*"It turned out to be a very good forum for the EDC to establish the relationship we now have with the community."*

— Glenn Landis

# – 6 –
# The Downtown Office

Once the Buffer Zone Controversy, as it came to be known, had been put to rest, progress on the new EROS Data Center building proceeded rapidly. Final drawings and specifications were well under way by the fall of 1971. The plan was to let bids just after the first of the year and begin construction in the spring of 1972.

In the meantime, members of the Development Foundation were hard at work on two fronts. First, they were negotiating the complex lease/purchase agreement of the Center with the federal government. Foundation members, with the aid of their attorney Russ Greenfield, worked closely with Bill Schmidt on this intricate legal document. The arrangement allowed the Foundation to build and retain ownership of the building, and lease it to the federal government for a period of 20 years. At the end of that time, the government would assume full ownership of the EDC.

*"[Countless] hours were spent in the Development Foundation offices writing and searching financial, legal, and construction documents...this was...many times the most frustrating aspect of the Development Foundation's involvement in EROS."*

— Dave Stenseth

Second, while the legal technicalities of the lease agreement were being sorted out, the Foundation went looking for money with which to pay for the building's construction. The members approached many potential sources, but the most favorable deal, a loan in the amount of $5.5 million, came from First National Bank of St. Paul, in St. Paul, Minnesota.

*"Yeah, the Development Foundation borrowed all that money and signed for it. I told Dave [Stenseth] 'if this backfires, we've got to get out of town!'"*

— Russ Pohl

Meanwhile, Glenn Landis was shuttling between Sioux Falls and Washington, D.C., busily organizing the interim Data Center. He also hired a number of additional people from within the federal government (the Nixon Administration had put a freeze on hiring any new federal employees) to form the core of the Center's staff.

Don Carney became Deputy Chief, working under Chief Glenn Landis. Jim McCord stayed on to become head of the Photo Lab, with Tom Lee and Scott Frazeur rounding out its staff. Bill Campbell, Fredericka (Freddie) Simon, Don Zoller, Bill Sowers, and Rebecca Faircloth formed the Data Management Branch. Gary Selner, R.J. Thompson, John Zabel, Sam Priebe, Linda Sowers, Al Hepner, and Ed Green made up the Computer Center Branch — officially known as the Sioux Falls Computation Branch of the Computer Center Division of USGS (the branch didn't officially become an organizational element under the Center Chief until 1973). The heart of the computer operation was to be an IBM 360-30 computer, received from the USGS Astrogeology Office in Flagstaff, Arizona. It was available essentially for the cost of transportation, but with a total memory capacity of only 64,000 bytes!

*"It [the IBM 360-30] was a big box of equipment, but a fairly small computer that probably couldn't do a tenth of what I can do with my laptop today. "*

— R.J. Thompson

## The Downtown Office

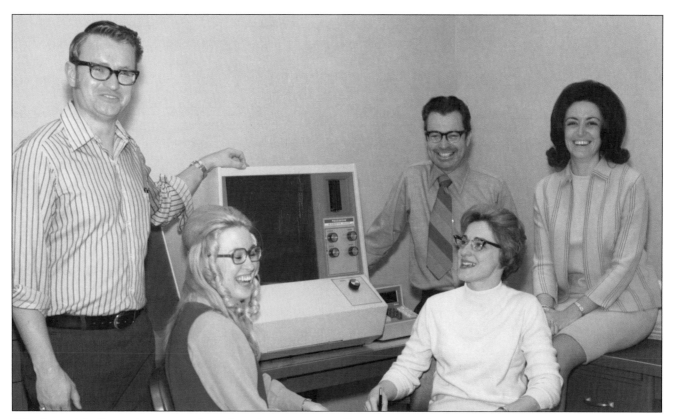

*Members of the Data Management Branch at the Downtown Office pose for a photo. (Left to right: Bill Sowers, Karla Sprenger, Bill Campbell, Freddie Simon, Rebecca Faircloth)*

*R.J. Thompson, one of the members of the original Computer Center Branch at the Downtown Office*

Once the essential staff were in place, all that was needed was a building to house the interim offices and photo processing laboratory. City officials offered several sites around Sioux Falls, including an abandoned airport terminal. But the final choice was the Soo Hudson Building, recently vacated by the Northwestern Bell Telephone Company in the city's downtown area, at the corner of 10th Street and Dakota Avenue. It was connected by a walkway to a rather dilapidated adjacent building, which was slated to be destroyed, and, therefore, could be converted into photo labs without too much difficulty. At long last, the Center had a home.

The Downtown Office, as it came to be called, officially opened its doors on September 28, 1971. It was a rather unusual "opening." During a press conference that afternoon, Landis took phone calls using one of the office's two phones that sat on the bare floor. There wasn't a desk in sight.

While local contractors began converting the building next door into a state-of-the-art photo lab, the staff moved into the Soo Hudson Building. The first piece of equipment to come through the doors was the IBM 360-30 computer. Designing the parameters of a remotely sensed image data base was one of the first challenges addressed by the Computer Branch. The IBM system had no facility for interactive development, and so the staff had to do everything "from scratch." In designing software, they wrote out code on coding sheets — or sometimes on the backs of envelopes — and then keypunched it into program cards.

*"...We'd talk about doing things like data bases, and image files and stuff like that — we didn't even know what the terms meant. We did some dumb things, I mean, we invested a lot of time and effort in things that later on we threw away. But we were learning, we were learning quick."*
— R.J. Thompson

Now that the Center had a base of operations, the time had come to hire additional people to fill out the staff. In November, 1971, Gail Hanson, fresh out of college, was hired as the Center's first secretary.

*"I was 20. It was my first real job. I walked in and there was a table, with a typewriter on it, and the phone was on the floor, with the cord stretched across the room. There was no furniture, nothing; it was just bare. There was a men's room. The women's restroom was full of photo processing equipment...so several times a day I got to visit the ladies' room at the Rite Spot Cafe just next door!"*
— Gail Hanson

Because of the hiring freeze that had been imposed by the federal government, however, it was clear from the outset that most of the new staff were going to have to come from the local area. Landis and the other managers felt that the activities at the Data Center would be so unique that it would be best to train a group of inexperi-

*At work on the IBM 360-30*

*EROS Program officials pose outside the Downtown Office. The Rite Spot Cafe can be seen down the street on the right. (Left to right: Charles Robinove, Arch Parker, Glenn Landis, William Pecora, John DeNoyer)*

construction, he used his own studio as the site for instruction. When advertisements came out in the local papers, dozens of people applied and were interviewed for the photography training opportunity. Eventually fifteen eligible candidates were selected and began their training on January 1, 1972. For six weeks they submerged themselves in the art of photography, learning how to mix chemicals, develop film, and make prints and enlargements.

> *"Bill Seward had a studio in Sioux Falls; he had taught photography at Augustana College, so he used his curriculum for that and condensed it for us...down into six weeks. We'd have the classroom part of it upstairs... and then we'd go down into the basement to work with chemicals and equipment."*
> — Diane Matzke

*Glenn Landis (seated) answers the phone during the press conference on "opening day" at the Downtown Office.*

*A glimpse into the entrance of the Downtown Office, where Lois Schulte answers the phone*

enced people from the ground up in the areas of photo processing, aerial photograph interpretation and map reading.

Money to train this new work force wasn't in the budget, however. That dilemma was quickly resolved when Landis learned that he could get people hired and trained through the Work Incentive (WIN) Program, a federal program designed to get unemployed people off the local welfare roles. Job Service of South Dakota agreed to coordinate training programs in photographic reproduction and data management for two groups of people hired under the WIN program.

Bill Seward, a local photographer, was hired to teach the photography training classes. Since the labs at the Data Center were still under

For most in the WIN group, the opportunity to work at the Center was a life-changing one, the chance to embark on a new career. There was a strong sense of camaraderie within the group, a feeling that everyone was participating in something grand and exciting. The management staff, in turn, couldn't have been more pleased with the performance of the WIN trainees and their unflagging work ethic. The new recruits possessed the same "whatever is required, we will do it" spirit that South Dakota politicians and Sioux Falls community leaders had exhibited in bringing the Data Center to the area.

*"I had come out from Washington, D.C., and I'd never been to the Midwest. When people there said 'Good Morning!' they actually meant it! The local people were just so friendly and sincere and hard-working."*
— Leo Braconnier

Shortly after the opening of the Downtown Office, shipments of film — negatives of historic aerial photographs used in map making — had begun arriving from the various USGS Mapping Centers. Most of the film had simply been piled up, awaiting a time when it could be sorted, cata-loged and shelved. In early January, 1972, not long after the WIN photo team started their training, disaster struck the offices. After temperatures plummeted to -30° F overnight, water pipes burst on the third floor of the Soo Hudson Building. When the staff arrived the following morning, they found fire trucks parked outside the entrance, ice coating the front windows, and several inches of water on the floor.

*"Someone had been up on the roof, working, and had come back in and forgotten to latch the door flap that went to the roof. The wind blew it open and froze the pipes. When I got there, Glenn was there and the firemen were sweeping up water...it had come from the top floor clear down to where we were on the first floor."*
— Fredericka "Freddie" Simon

The computer room had escaped damage, but the offices and the room where the irreplaceable aerial photography negatives had been stored were saturated with ice and water. Everyone pitched in to help, opening up the cans and stringing the film out to dry. Thanks to quick action on everyone's part, very little film was

*Glenn "Curly" Wachob, in the Photo Lab at the Downtown Office*

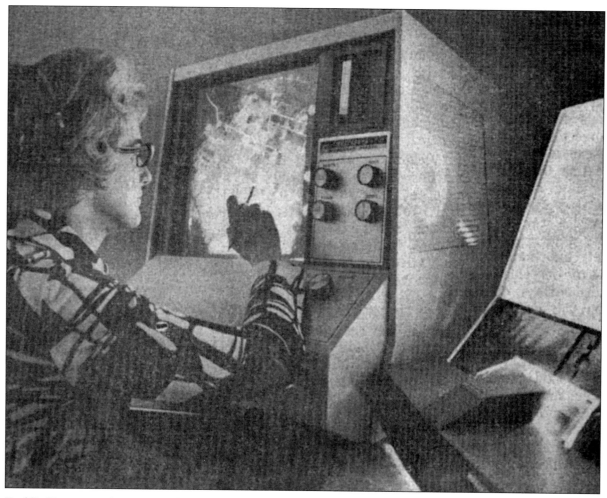

*Freddie Simon examines an aerial photograph on a microfilm reader.*

actually damaged. That left the task of weeding through stacks of wet papers, mopping up, and scrubbing down the walls. Within a few days, however, life in the Downtown Office was almost back to normal.

By early spring, the Photo Lab was completed and WIN trainees began processing requests for prints of the aerial photo negatives that now lined the Center's shelves. Cleanliness was essential inside the Photo Lab. The staff wore white gloves, lab coats — with no pockets, which could catch lint — cloth booties, cloth caps and hair nets (and in some cases, beard nets). Even the wearing of cosmetics was discouraged, to lessen the chance that particles of powder or flakes of mascara might fall onto film negatives and result in blemishes on the final products.

In March, 1972, the WIN Program hired Tom Earley to instruct the second group of WIN trainees in the basics of aerial photography, photo interpretation, and data handling. The group dug into the task of putting into the computer data base all of the information about the film that was arriving in great quantities, and setting up the logistics of archiving that film to make it easily retrievable. These were the early days of data processing, the era of computer cards, keypunching, and tractor-tread print-outs.

*"Back then you had sheets, encoding sheets, that had different columns for information like film type, the number of frames, storage location and so on. There were thousands of rolls of film that had come in...all boxed up and sitting there. Our job was to take it out of the boxes, encode it, give it a storage location and put it on the shelf. Later the keypunch operator would have to punch the data [from the encoding sheets] onto keypunch cards."*

— Diane Krell

When both groups of WIN trainees finished their respective courses of instruction, the graduates were offered full time jobs with the Data Center. However, because of the hiring freeze and budget restraints, the positions were classified as WAE (While Actually Employed), meaning workers were paid only for time spent on the job, and that they would receive no benefits of any kind. Despite such disappointing terms of employment, every one of the WIN training program graduates accepted the positions they were offered.

It wasn't long before the Data Center was humming within its cramped quarters. The Photo Lab was perfecting its art, the data base was growing, and film was being cataloged and archived. Already there were some 400,000 frames of aerial photo negatives on the shelves. It often seemed as if there was a never-ending stream of problems to be solved and challenges to be met during these early days at the Downtown Office. But an indomitable can-do attitude pervaded the facility. Despite limited resources, the staff worked long hours enthusiastically, anxious to be ready to do whatever was needed when the ERTS–1 satellite imagery began to arrive.

*"...Much of it was fly-by-the-seat-of-your-pants, in terms of doing things. A lot of creativity, a lot of 'How do we get this done?' and 'Let's go do it.' People had a lot of fun. I think in any organization in its early days there are fewer rules, and that makes it easier to just go do things."*

— Tom Earley

By this time, the agreements between the Sioux Falls Development Foundation and the federal government had been negotiated and signed. The loan for the proposed EROS Data Center facility had been secured and bids let for the building's construction. Lueder Construction Company of Omaha, Nebraska, submitted the lowest bid and was selected to be the primary contractor. Sioux Valley Electric Cooperative, headquartered in Colman, South Dakota, was to provide electric power to the Center. General Manager Virgil Herriott, Assistant Manager Jim Kiley, and Board Chairman Ray Johnson worked closely with the EDC planning team during this time. Now it was just a matter of waiting for winter to end so that construction could begin on the new facility.

*Employees in the Data Management Branch pose in front of shelves stacked with film canisters during the summer of 1972. (Left to right: Rolly Nelson, Tom Earley, Dee Schryver, Don Zoller, Geneva Kluck, Diane Krell, Dwayne Wipf, Betty Machmiller)*

### The Downtown Office

*The construction contract for the new EROS Data Center is signed on May 1, 1972. (Left to right: Russ Greenfield, Del Huddleston, project manager for Lueder Construction Company, Al Schock, Dave Stenseth)*

Ground-breaking ceremonies for the new EROS Data Center were set for April 14, 1972. On April 13, as a prelude to the official ceremonies that would follow, tours of the Downtown Office were given during which the Center staff explained to visitors the workings of the computer center, the film storage facilities, and showed off the Photo Lab. That night, a banquet was held at the downtown Holiday Inn hotel where 500 people listened to addresses by William Pecora, now Undersecretary of the Department of the Interior, and William Radlinski, the associate director of the USGS. Fittingly, Al Schock was Master of Ceremonies.

April 14, 1972, dawned cold and windy, as winter was just beginning to loosen its grip on the region. Yet nearly a thousand spectators turned out for the mid-morning ground-breaking ceremonies. Sioux Valley Electric set up a huge canvas tent, ordinarily used for their annual membership meetings, in which the crowd huddled to escape the wind. Spectators listened to speeches by William Pecora, William Fischer (now EROS Program Manager), and John DeNoyer, the Director of the

EROS Program Office in Washington, D.C. Local politicians and civic leaders were also on hand and on the podium.

*"It [EROS] is the largest Earth scientific experiment ever undertaken by man and possibly the most significant."*
— William A. Fischer, speaking at the 1972 ground-breaking ceremonies

An announcement was made that several roads leading to the site would be renamed that day in honor of three individuals who had played key roles in bringing the EROS Data Center into existence. The road leading east from Highway 77 toward the Data Center was named "Mundt Highway" in honor of South Dakota Senator Karl Mundt. The main road off Highway 121 was christened "Young Boulevard" after North Dakota Senator Milton Young, and the circular drive that would one day lead to the building's front entrance became "Pecora Way."

Al Schock, again directing activities as Master

*Sioux Valley Electric employees erect the tent that will be used at the ground-breaking ceremonies.*

*Gib Kringen urges his two mules forward as William Pecora (left, wearing hat), Merlyn Veren, and Glenn Landis lean into the plow.*

of Ceremonies, had arranged an interesting variation on the traditional approach to a ground breaking. The earth wasn't to be upturned with a shovel, but by a mule-drawn plow. Gilbert "Gib" Kringen, who farmed just north of the EDC site, furnished both the plow and a pair of mules to pull it.

After the speeches, Schock and Pecora led the way out of the tent and over to the spot where the mules stood waiting. The audience crowded around as key officials clutched the worn wooden handles of the old plow. At Kringen's urging, the mules leaned into the harness and the plow sliced into the cold ground, exposing the first black earth on the future site of the new EROS Data Center building.

*Pecora – and the mules – pose for photos beside the freshly turned earth.*

*The Delta rocket carrying the ERTS–1 satellite begins its journey into space.*

# – 7 –
# ERTS–1 and the EROS Data Center

A s construction began on the new building, the launch of ERTS–1 was just months away. After years of research and experimentation, NASA had decided on two different types of imaging sensors to be used aboard the satellite: a Return Beam Vidicon (RBV) and a Multi-Spectral Scanner (MSS). The RBV worked rather like a combination of three television cameras. The MSS system used a rotating mirror and several detectors to scan the Earth's surface. Each detector was designed to sense a different part of the spectrum of light being reflected off the planet. Those "spectral bands" ranged from visible green light to invisible near-infrared. Each detector could be used to record information about certain types of resources, such as vegetation. Images produced by the different detectors could be combined to create rather eerie looking "false color" pictures of the planet.

Hopes for the success of ERTS–1 as a tool to learn more about the planet's terrestrial features and natural resources were pinned primarily on the RBV system. Researchers assumed from the beginning that the images produced by the RBV would be more dependable and valuable than those returned by the MSS system. In fact, the MSS was regarded as a strictly experimental device for collecting data about the brightness of objects on the Earth's surface.

By the middle of summer, the ERTS–1 satellite was being readied for launch out at Vandenberg Air Force Base in California. Tragically, on July 19, 1972, only two days before the long-awaited satellite was set to head out into orbit, William Pecora died unexpectedly at age 59 as a result of complications following rather routine surgery. Pecora's sudden death was a terrible blow to the EROS Program. For years, he had been one of its most dynamic and enthusiastic proponents.

*"Bill died just days before the first satellite was scheduled to be launched. The Secretary of the Interior, Rogers Morton, called me and said, 'What are we going to do?' And I said, 'Send it up!' Bill's interest, influence and drive was still there even after his death."*
— Wyn Pecora, widow of William Pecora

Several days before the launch at Vandenberg, plans were made to send a delegation from Sioux Falls to witness the great event. The Sioux

*The Sioux Falls delegation heads to Mission Control for the launch of ERTS–1.*

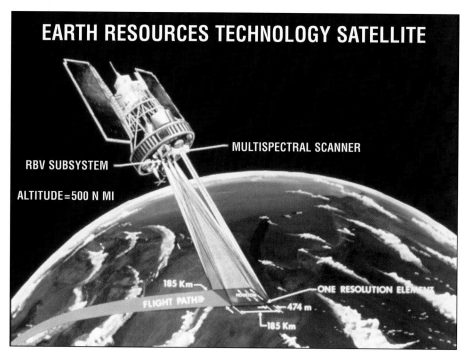

**EARTH RESOURCES TECHNOLOGY SATELLITE**

MULTISPECTRAL SCANNER

RBV SUBSYSTEM

ALTITUDE=500 N MI

185 Km

FLIGHT PATH

ONE RESOLUTION ELEMENT

474 m

185 Km

*An illustration showing ERTS–1 in orbit and how its two sensors will capture images of the planet's surface*

Falls Development Foundation commandeered a C-54 transport plane from the South Dakota Air National Guard and invited about thirty individuals who had been instrumental in getting the EROS Data Center project off the ground to join the delegation. Dave Stenseth was in charge of the group, which included members of the Foundation and the Sioux Falls Chamber of Commerce, along with a number of city, county and state officials.

The day before the scheduled launch, the C-54 took off from Sioux Falls with the delegation on board. Everything went smoothly at first, but not long into the flight the plane encountered severe, unrelenting turbulence. Needless to say, the flight quickly turned into every traveler's worst nightmare, as almost everyone on board became violently airsick. Glenn Landis and Russ Pohl were there to meet the delegation when they landed, and were no doubt relieved that they had arrived by other means to witness the upcoming launch. Al Schock and Sioux Valley Electric's Jim Kiley were also on hand.

The unlucky delegation had plenty of time to recover from their ordeal, however. The ERTS–1 launch was delayed first once, then twice. By the morning of Sunday, July 23, everyone was beginning to wonder if the rocket would ever get off

the ground. Finally, after a third, albeit brief delay, the Delta rocket thundered aloft, carrying the ERTS–1 satellite into orbit. After all the waiting, the actual event was something of a disappointment, since within seconds after lift-off, the rocket disappeared into the low cloud cover.

*"When it went off, it was a non-event. Sort of like if you bought a big fireworks rocket and your mother wouldn't let you fire it for a few days, and finally she says 'OK,' and you put a match to it and PFFFTTTT! — it's gone!"*
— Glenn Landis

The launch may have been anticlimactic, but the news from NASA in the hours and days to follow was exciting and encouraging. The satellite had achieved a perfect polar orbit, sweeping down from the Arctic to Antarctica and back every 103 minutes. From its vantage point in space, ERTS–1 passed over the same spot, at almost precisely the same hour, every 18 days. The advantages of that arrangement were twofold: first, there would be little difference in lighting from image to image, and second, because sequential images were created of the same location, ERTS–1 would make it relatively easy for researchers to spot changes in the planet's features over time.

Less than two days after the launch, in its 27th orbit, ERTS–1 began sending back images from the RBV system. Hours later, the MSS began sending back data as well. Images from the satellite were beamed down to receiving stations in Fairbanks, Alaska, in Mojave, California, and in Greenbelt, Maryland, and then relayed to NASA's Goddard Space Flight Center in Greenbelt. There, the electronic images were converted into photographic form and the resulting film was flown to the EROS Data

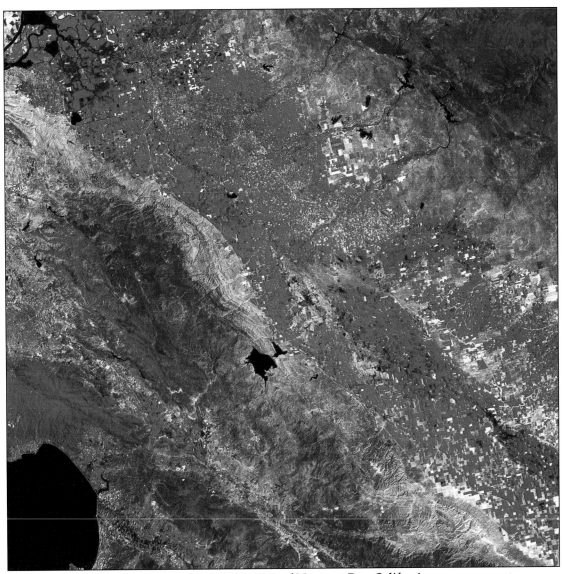

*One of the first ERTS–1 images, taken July 25, 1972, of Monterey Bay, California*

Center in Sioux Falls, where it could be used to produce images of the planet's surface.

The first photo negatives from ERTS–1 arrived in Sioux Falls less than a week after the launch. Stan Addis, a member of the EROS Program Office in Washington, flew to Sioux Falls with the negatives in hand. At the Downtown Office, with television cameras rolling, Glenn Landis officially accepted the first ERTS–1 image on behalf of the EDC.

After the press left, the negatives were taken back into the Photo Lab for processing. To everyone's horror, it quickly became apparent that the negatives were nearly opaque. Only after herculean efforts that ran into the wee hours of the morning was a somewhat satisfactory print made.

*"We took the film into the photo lab and got the shock of our lives. In the vernacular of the photo industry, the negative was 'bulletproof'! We could not get enough light through the opaque negative to make a print, even with 10 or 20 minute exposures....We were finally able to blast enough light through the negative to make a print to show the media and pontificate about the significance of the Earth-imaging achievement, but we were shaken with the knowledge that there was no way we could mass produce images for the public with twenty minute exposure times in the lab.... [Later] we solved the problem by contact printing the film to a lower density negative for our production use."*

— Glenn Landis

That first photograph — an RBV image of the Dallas-Fort Worth area — was splashed on the front pages of newspapers across the country. The people of the United States, and those of many other nations, got their first look at what ERTS–1 could do. Yet to the surprise of those closely associated with the EROS Program, the RBV images coming from the satellite turned out to be disappointingly "splotchy," while those from the MSS were not only beautiful pictures of the Earth's surface, but extremely accurate for research purposes. Interest in the RBV system quickly waned as a result, and NASA ultimately ceased routine processing of RBV data.

With the arrival of that first ERTS image at the Data Center, however, the flow of film from the Goddard Space Flight Center to Sioux Falls began in earnest. And as the film came in, so did the orders for satellite photos and other images. Orders poured in from across the country and from all segments of society, from government and university scientists doing research on natural resources to prospectors searching for mineral deposits to private citizens anxious to get a satellite picture of their farm or house.

*"We got to know the guys at Ozark [Airlines] really well. We got rolls of film almost every day...we'd bring them back, log them in, get them into the system, and they'd be available to make prints."*

— Tom Earley

*"There would be a press release somewhere in the United States, and...we'd have stacks of paper all over, everybody's desk would be piled high with requests."*

— Karla Sprenger

Ads in national magazines promoted the ERTS–1 images, often with headlines asking readers: "Do you want to see a picture of your hometown — from 500 miles up?" followed by the address or phone number of the EDC. Every time such an ad or article about the satellite came out, requests for photos and images flooded in. Those requests ranged from the seriously scientific to the truly bizarre.

*"You'd get so many different questions... customers would ask things that would just baffle you. Many wanted to know what the satellites could do. There were people who wanted to find something underwater — they would call in and say: 'This boat went down on some canal with treasure on it, and I want to find it.' Or somebody would want to see a picture of themselves in their driveway, and they'd ask what time the satellite went over so they could look up and wave."*

— Juanita Roland

**PEEKABOO, IT SEES YOU**
Although you probably didn't know it, the world's most expensive commercial camera went into orbit on July 23, 1972, when the Earth Resources Technology Satellite was placed in space. To get more info on how to order pics of your favorite 13,225-square-mile area, write: EROS Data Center, Sioux Falls, South Dakota 57198. Smile, you're on candid satellite.

*An advertisement from a 1972 issue of **Playboy** magazine encourages readers to order satellite images of Earth.*

More staff were added at the Downtown Office to process orders, send out information, and handle the steady flow of film coming from ERTS–1 via Goddard. Descriptive data about all the incoming ERTS images (as well as much of the backlog of aerial photography at the Center) were entered on an almost daily basis into a data base on the IBM 360-30 known as the Main Image File, or MIF. When an inquiry arrived at the EDC, the request would be run against the Main Image File and a computer listing — a printed list on tractor-drive paper — would be generated that indicated all of the various images in the data base that met the customer's specifications. If staff members suspected that a customer was seeking something that was not yet in the MIF, they would do a manual search of the hard copy index of images to determine what, if anything, was available to fit the request.

The printed list was then sent out to the customer, who made a selection and returned the order form, complete with payment. Information about the order was then entered into the computer and a production order was generated and sent to the Photo Lab.

Many of the letters that arrived at the Center were sent by people who simply wanted to know more about this new technology, or who needed guidance as to how to go about placing an order. These sorts of inquiries were passed on to staff members who sent out information packets, complete with personalized letters. The letter writing was done on what was, for the time, a relatively high-tech machine: the IBM Selectric magnetic tape typewriter. Mag-tape typewriters had a primitive monitor and tape drive into which a magnetic tape cartridge — about the size of a videocassette — could be inserted. Blocks of type could be stored on the tape, recalled onto the screen when needed, and then automatically inserted into a letter being typed.

Because so many requests were for similar

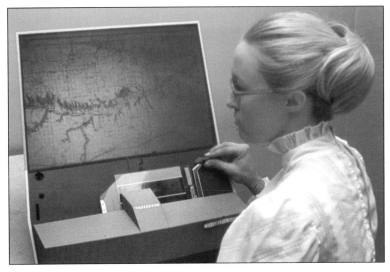

*Karla Sprenger uses a microfilm reader to examine satellite images.*

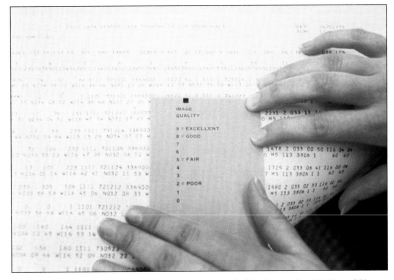

*A computer listing of satellite images available from the EDC to fill a customer request*

kinds of information, the staff in the User Services department created stock paragraphs on the mag-tape cartridges and then composed their letters by assembling various paragraphs, with a few individual touches thrown in here and there, into a final product.

*"Rita Tornow, who was the IBM Typewriter expert, and I soon discovered that if we were ever going to make a dent in those mountains of letters, we would have to write up dozens of 'generic' paragraphs.... I'd compose a few original sentences, then 'insert paragraph 7,' a few more sentences, then 'insert paragraph 4,' etc..."*

— Phyllis Wiepking

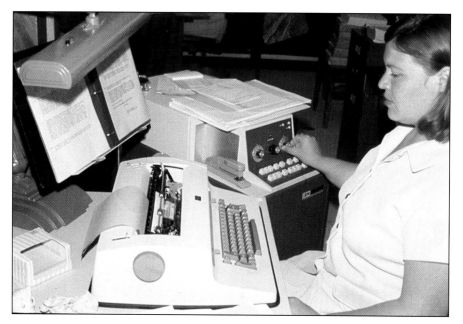

*Rita Tornow works at a mag-tape typewriter.*

that no one ever caught up. Many employees took work home with them at night or stayed after hours with no compensation. On more than one occasion, Chief Glenn Landis caught employees punching out on the time clock at the end of the day, and then returning to complete a job they felt compelled to finish. It also wasn't unusual for the entire staff to work together to complete a particularly urgent task.

A somewhat similar device, the magnetic-card (mag-card) typewriter, was used for order processing in those early days, a job that was largely done by hand and was very labor intensive. During the summer of 1972, however, the Computer Branch set to work trying to interface the mag-card typewriter with the computer so that orders could be entered into it remotely from User Services. The IBM manual indicated that such a connection might be possible, but there was no interface software in the computer's operating system. So once again the computer staff did "whatever it took" and wrote their own. The day the link was forged between the computer and the mag-card typewriters was a significant breakthrough.

*"We were under a lot of pressure and had a lot of things going on. We were working with old equipment, with cast-offs from other federal agencies and departments.... It was a matter of sink or swim, and I don't think many people [in D.C.] really expected us to swim. But we did, and it was that outstanding work ethic that made it happen."*
— Freddie Simon

And so the inquiries and orders rolled in, and photos and letters and information packets flowed out. The workload was so overwhelming

*"You did whatever anybody asked you to do. You never heard 'Oh, that's not my job,' or 'I don't do that.' The lowest to the highest did pretty much everything."*
— Rhonda Watkins

The downtown staff worked hard, but they also took time to celebrate moments of triumph, from solutions to technical problems and the acquisition of new equipment to the meeting or surpassing of production goals. Camaraderie among the young, energetic group often extended beyond the boundaries of the Soo Hudson Building. Many employees routinely went out to dinner together after work and socialized in the evenings, especially on Friday nights at local night spots in downtown Sioux Falls.

*"We celebrated everything. Every accomplishment, big or small...every new thing... because we started with nothing."*
— Gail Hanson

One of the reasons that ERTS–1 images were suddenly in such demand was that they were surprisingly good. The resolution of the MSS images, in particular, had exceeded everyone's expectations. And in just the first few months following the launch, those satellite images had already revealed startling new information about natural resources and geological features on the planet's surface. For instance, William Fischer and others reported that new sources of underground water were discovered in several parts of the United States, and a previously undetected fault was identified near the San Francisco Bay area.

Successes and surprises like these validated the original claims made by Pecora, Fischer and others as to the value of the EROS Program, and led NASA to push ahead with plans for a second satellite. Since ERTS–1 was expected to be operational for only about a year, those involved with the program wanted to move ahead with ERTS–2 as quickly as possible so there would be no break in the steady stream of data being beamed down to Earth.

But the success of the EROS Program involved much more than simply receiving

images of the planet's surface from space. The real value of those images lay in how they could be used to better explore, monitor, and manage Earth's natural resources. Thus, the Program's managers were aware from the beginning of the need to educate potential users, especially resource managers from federal and state agencies, as to the value of remote sensing from space. In so doing, they would not only introduce the benefits of this new technology to diverse user groups, but would also create a growing market for satellite imagery.

The challenge of training potential users fell initially to Don Kulow, who arrived from USGS headquarters to set up what was initially called the Professional Services section of the EDC. Kulow had taught photo interpretation at the University of West Virginia, and he enthusiastically put together the first training course in

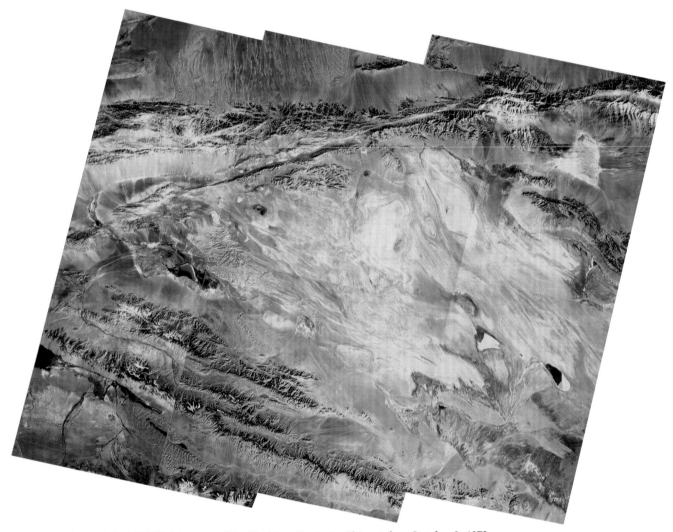

*A series of mosaicked ERTS–1 images of the Tsaidam Basin in China taken October 2, 1972*

remote sensing data interpretation at the Downtown Office for scientists from several agencies of the Department of the Interior. The class was held on the second floor of the Soo Hudson Building, where space had been rented for the training offices, and where Rita Flanery handled the secretarial duties.

In order to acquaint members of the Sioux Falls community with remote sensing technology and its potential, Kulow also offered an evening training class in photointerpretation using historic and current aerial photos of the Sioux Falls area. The participants, who ranged from real estate agents and business owners to lawyers and city engineers, were shown how to use the photos to trace the growth of neighborhoods, identify locations for new businesses, and better discern relationships between transportation routes, waterways, and other features. The class was a great success and helped establish considerable rapport between the EDC and the Sioux Falls community.

Tragically, Don Kulow died within a year of his arrival at the Data Center in February, 1973, a victim of the long-term effects of juvenile diabetes. The library of the new building was later named in his honor.

Other classes followed at the Data Center, including the first international training course. In June, 1973, thirty-three scientists and engineers from more than a dozen countries participated in a month-long remote sensing workshop led by Robert Reeves, Don Orr, and Jim Walden. The event was widely covered in local newspapers, and gave area residents their first glimpse of how the EDC would soon become a focal point for teams of scientists from around the globe.

*"It was quite interesting to have those foreign visitors come to the Center downtown. My family and I had several of them over to our house for dinner. They were very bright people, some from little postage-stamp countries that we knew little about. Most could speak some English, but there were occasionally language barriers."*

*— Rita Flanery*

*Don Kulow taught the first training course in remote sensing data interpretation at the EDC.*

As the summer progressed, the modern and spacious structure that was to become the EDC's new home northeast of Sioux Falls was nearing completion. Roads to the site were widened, paved, and in some cases, raised. A water transmission line was built from Sioux Falls to the site, to supply water of high enough quality for photo processing. Telephone service was supplied through underground cables from the nearby town of Garretson. Electricity came through two 69,000-volt transmission lines, built especially to handle the Center's enormous power needs by East River Electric Power Cooperative of Madison, South Dakota (Sioux Valley Electric's wholesale power supplier). The Cooperative's crews constructed an additional two miles of 12,470-volt underground lines between the "EROS substation" and the Center itself. (When the EDC began operations roughly two years later, it instantly became the largest energy consumer on Sioux Valley's lines, using as much electricity per month as 500 farms.)

Toward the end of June, in an informal ceremony, Al Schock, construction superintendent Del Huddleston and others lifted the building's 250-pound cornerstone into position. Afterwards, Schock announced to the press that the formal dedication of the new EROS Data Center would be held in August.

In July of 1973, the Professional Services section of the Downtown Office was the first to move into the building, under an agreement called "benevolent occupancy," in order to take control of the building, protect it from vandals, and oversee the final stages of finishing construction. The four-person Professional Services section made do with a few bits of surplus furniture. Without a building maintenance staff, they emptied their own trash, and with no operational phone system, as Don Orr put it: "It was pretty quiet out there." But the group wasn't entirely alone. That summer there was a plague of sand beetles roaming the countryside, and the new facility was literally crawling with them. With the dedication only a few weeks away, the building was repeatedly

fumigated in order to rid it of the creeping, scuttling pests before the big event during which crowds of people would be touring the facility.

*"That summer sand beetles literally overran the building. You couldn't walk down the halls without stepping on dozens of them. Each time the building was fumigated, clean-up crews would move through the halls the next day and sweep up bushels of dead beetles. Fortunately, we got rid of them before the dedication."*

— Don Orr

On August 6, the day before the dedication, area residents had a chance to learn what would be happening out at the Center at a public information seminar held in Sioux Falls. During the all-day event, EROS experts were on hand to explain the program, remote sensing, and satellite imagery in "plain, simple, everyday language." Those who attended heard how the new $5.5 million facility would become a

*The new EROS Data Center takes shape northeast of Sioux Falls.*

*The building's cornerstone is set in place.*

national center for processing and distributing satellite and aircraft images of the Earth. They also learned that the EDC would be a training site where scientists and managers would receive hands-on experience in learning how to utilize remotely sensed data in studying and managing Earth's natural resources.

The following day, August 7, 1973, under a blazing summer sun, nearly two thousand spectators gathered for the official dedication of the Karl E. Mundt Federal Building as the EROS Data Center. Secretary of the Interior Rogers C. B. Morton gave the main address, in which he described the EROS Program as the "first major dividend from America's space effort that can be shared by all mankind." Morton was assisted in the ribbon cutting ceremony by a little girl from the audience who was selected to represent the youth of the world. The event marked the real-

ization of a long-held dream for many who witnessed the ceremony that day. It also became the official founding day of the EROS Data Center, a date that would be celebrated annually in the years that followed.

> *"Bill was so thrilled during the ceremony that day. He kept saying, 'I never thunk it' over and over. Our little boy used to say that in kindergarten and the phrase was kind of a family joke. For Bill, the dedication and all that it represented was a dream come true."*
> — Blanche Fischer

Following the official ceremonies, the EDC opened its doors to the public. Visitors packed the corridors, peering at the photo lab equipment, getting their first chance to see the inside of this "space age" facility. Public interest was so

*Secretary of the Interior Rogers C. B. Morton gives the main address at the dedication of the EROS Data Center on August 7, 1973.*

strong, in fact, that a second open house was held several days later, when nearly five thousand people stood in long lines to listen to EDC scientists explain the operation of various pieces of equipment and to view slides and satellite images of the Earth.

There was excitement in the air during those hot August days. After years of struggling, first to bring the Center to South Dakota, and then to get it up and running in cramped, make-shift quarters, the EROS Data Center was ready to move into its new home, and begin a fresh chapter in its colorful history.

*Beneath the hot summer sun, more than two thousand people listen to the dedication ceremony speakers.*

## – 8 –
# A New Location, A New Direction

The fall of 1973 was a period of rapid and dramatic change at the EROS Data Center. At the same time that the staff of the Downtown Office began making preparations for the move into the new Karl E. Mundt federal building northeast of Sioux Falls, they also found themselves facing a major restructuring of the Center's organization and leadership.

One change came in the form of a private contractor, hired to employ and manage the on-site technical support staff. Earlier in the year it had become obvious that the existing staff of roughly seventy people was not nearly large enough to handle the rapidly expanding work load of processing, distributing and archiving the steady stream of satellite imagery coming from space. More people were needed, and quickly. Because federal restrictions on the hiring of new government employees were still in effect, however, the EROS Program Office had directed Glenn Landis to take the necessary steps to secure a private contractor to employ and oversee a considerably larger support staff.

Landis and others who had come from the USGS were a bit leery of this proposition. They were concerned that bringing in a private contractor at the Center might create a division in the work force, as it had at some other federal agencies, by putting contract employees on an unequal footing with their government counterparts. But the edict from the Program Office couldn't be ignored.

So in June of 1973, the Center management had begun hammering out the details of a contract, setting up parameters for operation, delineating responsibilities, and defining which positions at the EDC would be held by federal employees, and which would be under the jurisdiction of the contractor. During this time, the staff was instructed to stop taking work home at night, so that normal workloads and the amount of time it took to complete various tasks could

be better assessed. That request flew in the face of the local work ethic.

*"...there were some of us who snuck work home anyway. We were more concerned that the customers got what they needed when they needed it...."*

—Rita Tornow

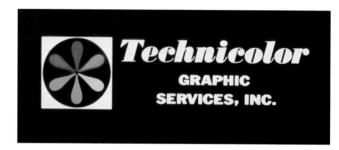

*Technicolor Graphics Services, Inc., became the EDC's first technical support contractor in the autumn of 1973.*

Once the details of the contract were worked out, bids were let and over the next few weeks six proposals were received. Technicolor, Inc. was selected and awarded the technical support contract in September, 1973. (Within two years, its name was changed to Technicolor Graphics Services, Inc.) In the months that followed, several other contracts were also awarded to smaller firms whose employees were responsible for building operations and maintenance, custodial services, and security at the EDC.

A second major change was announced that same month, this time in the Center's management. EROS Program managers asked Glenn Landis, who had served as Center Chief for more than two years, to focus his skills and expertise on the overwhelming tasks associated with data production and distribution, and hired Allen H. Watkins to join the staff as Chief of the EDC. Watkins had strong ties to NASA and the space program, and had most recently been Deputy Program Manager for NASA's Earth

Resources Program at the Johnson Space Center in Houston. Initially reluctant to accept the position, Watkins was eventually swayed by what he saw as a unique opportunity to lead the EDC in new directions, and by the caliber of the staff and their obvious dedication to the work they were doing.

*"...You don't often get a chance to build your own thing from something very small to whatever you have confidence that it can be.... I thought in many ways it would be a real challenge."*

— Al Watkins

Amid these developments, the downtown staff was faced with the challenge of moving offices, a computer system, a photo lab, and an entire archive in such a way as to cause a minimal amount of disruption in the flow of data and images in and out of the EDC. The Professional Services section had been in the building for a number of weeks. The next section to make the move was User Services, and when they did, an unexpected event added to the chaos. The Eastman Kodak company — unbeknownst to the staff — had chosen this particular moment to do the Center and the EROS Program a favor by running a series of large advertisements in *Scientific American* and some fifty other national magazines. The ads encouraged readers who wanted "pictures of home from 567 miles up" to write or call the new EROS Data Center north of Sioux Falls (not the Downtown Office) to request them. The staff learned on a Thursday near the end of September that the ads would be released the following Monday. In order to be ready for the flood of orders everyone knew would ensue, User Services was moved in a 48-hour blitz over the weekend. And as expected, the phones started ringing first thing Monday morning, and the requests for satellite images poured in. For weeks afterward, User Services was inundated with orders that overflowed from desks and shelves onto piles on the floor.

*Al Watkins*

*Know the land and the people*

For sale by the U.S. Department of the Interior at modest prices:

## Pictures of home from 567 miles up

Some time between 9:30 and 10 a.m. once every 18 days, NASA's ERTS (Earth Resources Technology Satellite) looks down on you and transmits to earth what it sees. Its purpose is to guide plans for living wisely on our globe, to preserve its glory for our children and our children's children.

The plans concern such fundamentals as water, food, energy, minerals, forests, the possibility of natural and unnatural disasters, and human interaction. Such fundamentals need to be understood on levels ranging from grade school to think tank. Anybody can have any ERTS picture for professional or business purposes, or even just to pretty up a corner of the recreation room. Proceed as follows:

Write EROS Data Center, Sioux Falls, S.D. 57198 or, if you want immediate personal service and don't mind the phone toll, call 605-594-6511 between 7 a.m. and 7 p.m. Central Time. Indicate geographical area and what you have in mind.

If you want to be able to see individual buildings and maybe the old swimming hole,

ERTS flies too high for you. Fortunately a big computer at Sioux Falls will know instantly whether, instead of pictures that cover 115 miles on a side (that's 13,225 square miles), EROS can offer you a picture of the place made from 5,000 feet in 1936, for example. Perhaps a Gemini astronaut or Skylab photographed the area. The computer will know. The computer will even know how much was under cloud each time ERTS passed over.

The EROS price list reflects just the cost of reproducing the photographs, not the cost of flying satellites and aircraft. A 9″ x 9″ black-and-white print, for example, is priced at $1.75 regardless of subject; a 40″ x 40″ color enlargement, $25. Duplicate negatives can be ordered. No copyright restrictions.

Just one request: Please don't write or call Kodak on EROS business. We're just running this advertising in order to alert you to an almost-free photographic dividend from the nation's investment. (Don't let that word "EROS" bother you. It stands for "Earth Resources Observation Systems.")

Wendy S. Hunter

**...down to earth**

Here is an easier picture to interpret than an infrared view from a satellite. *Friendship can be a valuable therapy* it says for a community organization seeking volunteers. It is one of some 300 photographs in *Help Your Community through Photography*, a new book that goes into much detail on how to go about helping others with your camera. "Try to borrow one if you don't have your own," says this Kodak publication. "You can use any camera to take good pictures, so don't buy a new one." Available in bookstores and photo stores, or for $5.95 as Publication AC-7 from Dept. 454, Kodak, Rochester, N.Y. 14650.

*Eastman Kodak helped promote ERTS–1 satellite images by running this and similar advertisements in national magazines in September, 1973.*

## A New Location, A New Direction

*Norm Doolittle moves film archives into the new building.*

Not long afterwards, the Computer Branch and the Administrative offices followed User Services to the new site. Moving out of cramped, rather dingy quarters into a brand new 116,000 square foot state-of-the-art facility was a welcome change. Suddenly there was room to spare. So much room, in fact, that initially the halls echoed and the few furnishings that made the trip over seemed lost in the huge new spaces. The IBM 360-30 stood alone in the spacious new computer room, looking very small indeed.

The last thing to be moved was the Photo Lab and the film archives. Thousands of film canisters were packed up in boxes, loaded onto a moving van and driven out — during an early winter snowstorm — to the new building.

*"I remember when we were moving film out here. It was snowing and here we were [in a pickup] following this semi...I could just imagine the semi going in the ditch with film cans spilling out all over the place."*
— Tom Earley

Throughout the fall of 1973, the size of the staff grew significantly. Most of the people who had been working downtown as WAE employees went to work for Technicolor, Inc., and many new faces soon joined the "downtowners." By the time the move into the new facility was completed in January, 1974, the total number of

EDC employees had risen to 210.

The transition to a contract situation went very smoothly, in large part because the Center management went to great lengths to insure that there was no visible difference between contract and government employees. They encouraged and reinforced a feeling of esprit de corps, of working toward a common goal. That sense of team spirit would serve the EDC well in the years that followed, in that it augmented the attitude already shared by the employees, one of being ready to do "whatever it took" to help the Center succeed in its mission.

*"We didn't want to be able to tell who was who. We were all working toward a common goal.... [A person wasn't] a contract employee or a government employee, but an EDC employee."*
— Glenn Landis

Up until this point in its history, the EDC had been primarily a photo reproduction laboratory, focused on processing, distributing and archiving remotely sensed images of the Earth. Now, as the dust from the move cleared, and the growing staff settled into their new home, Al Watkins felt the time was right for the EDC to expand its horizons and embark in a new direction. The founders of the EROS Program had shared a vision that the Center would one day be not merely an archive, but a dynamic facility in which scientists from many disciplines could develop new applications for remotely sensed data. Watkins wanted to bring to the EDC a level of scientific expertise that it did not have. And to accomplish this goal, he turned recruiter, and went out looking for talent.

*"In the [remote sensing] community, many felt that the real secret to making it go — not just the EROS Data Center, but the whole Earth resources/remote sensing program — was to get scientists involved and to build up a credible scientific work force."*
— Al Watkins

*EDC scientists pore over a satellite image. (Clockwise, left to right: Jim Nickerson, Al Hahn, Bill Anderson, Bill Draeger, Dave Carneggie, Jim Taranik)*

In the early 1970s, remote sensing research was still in an embryonic stage. There were only a few pockets of expertise in the field outside the federal government, mostly at major academic research universities, such as the University of California at Berkeley, the University of Michigan, Purdue University, Stanford University and a few others. These institutions maintained active research programs in aerial photo interpretation, satellite data acquisition and processing, and had major computer centers and large graduate student programs.

Initially, Watkins focused his recruiting efforts on Berkeley in particular, where the Forestry Department was renowned for its expertise in remote sensing as it applied to forest management, rangeland ecology, wildlife ecology, and natural resource monitoring. Watkins hired Gene Thorley, a recent graduate of the Berkeley program, who was at the time working for

NASA, and together the two men conspired to bring a half dozen other Berkeley graduates to the Center, including Don Lauer, Bill Draeger, and Dave Carneggie. Along with these Berkeley graduates, Wayne Rohde, Jim Taranik, Dave Greenlee, Fred Waltz, and several others joined an existing science staff that included Don Orr, Jim Walden, and Dennis Hood. Together, this team of young remote sensing scientists gave the EDC, in Watkins' words, "instant credibility" in academic, political and industrial circles, and with the public.

*"It looked like a wonderful opportunity to take our research results and translate them into practical applications. However, my wife, Carol, wasn't too keen on leaving sunny California. So I told her, 'We'll give it about two years and then move on....'"*

— Don Lauer

*"We all showed up within a couple of months…. As we sorted out what kinds of research and applications activities we wanted to do, we started selectively adding more staff."*

— Wayne Rohde

In July of 1974, ERTS–1 began its third year in orbit. The satellite had surprised everyone by continuing to function well beyond its original life expectancy of one year. This was a great relief to those involved with the EROS Program, because funding cuts and budget wars in Washington had forced NASA to postpone the launch of its replacement, ERTS–2, until early 1975. ERTS–1, the nation's first dedicated land remote sensing satellite, had certainly proved its usefulness in its two years of operation, becoming an invaluable tool for monitoring the Earth and its resources, both in the United States and abroad. Brazil and Canada had already built ground stations to receive data directly from the satellite when it passed over their respective countries. Plans for ground stations in other countries were also under way.

*Foreign visitors get a tour of the EROS Data Center.*

*The lobby of the EDC (circa 1975)*

Expectations were high, too, that the Data Center might soon be getting its own antenna that would enable it to receive data directly from satellites — and justify the Center's location in the middle of the country in the process. However, the wait for that elusive antenna was to prove to be a long one.

As 1974 came to a close, Data Center employees no doubt looked back in amazement at the enormous changes the organization had undergone in less than two years. There had been more than a four-fold increase in staff — nearly 300 people were employed by the Center at this point, with a payroll of $2.5 million. The number of aerial photographs and satellite

images in the archives was approaching 6 million, with roughly 12,000 images being added every month. Orders for remotely sensed data were flooding in, with production and sales reflecting a steady increase. And a team of cutting-edge researchers had been assembled at this "little data center on the prairie" where they were eager to begin exploring creative new applications for remotely sensed data, and to share their discoveries with users all over the world. The EROS Data Center was now poised to broaden its horizons and the scope of its mission and impact. The potential for growth and development seemed almost limitless, and the future was looking very bright.

# – 9 –
# Years of Expansion (1975-1978)

The year 1975 was the start of a period of tremendous growth and expansion at the EROS Data Center, and it began with two dramatic events: a Dakota blizzard, and a second satellite launch.

On Friday, January 10, 1975, one of the worst winter storms ever to hit southeastern South Dakota came screaming across the prairie. Aware of the approaching blizzard, but not its speed and intensity, Center managers announced that the building would close early that day. But not early enough, as it turned out. By the time the staff began heading home in mid-afternoon, the storm had already arrived with a fury that caught everyone by surprise. High winds drove falling snow almost horizontally across the open landscape, reducing visibility to near zero. The circular front drive (Pecora Way) and the road leading west to Highway 121 (Young Boulevard) kept drifting shut, despite the best efforts of the maintenance crews. Skidding and sliding, the majority of the departing cars and trucks eventually made it out to the highway. But the last few weren't as lucky, and became hopelessly mired in the ever-deepening snow. The thirty or so people who were unable to get out eventually abandoned their vehicles and headed back to the Center. There was nothing to do but find sanctuary in the building until the blizzard was over.

*"It was the worst storm I've ever seen...the temps were way below zero, so the windchills were killers. You couldn't see anything, it was atrocious. When you walked out the back doors [the employee entrance] you walked up a hill of snow that was like rock."*
— Tom Earley

Some of those trapped by the storm retreated to their offices and worked over that weekend, while others passed the time by reading and socializing, or watching football, as it was Superbowl weekend. One group formed a Canasta club, after first making up a deck of hand-drawn, hand-cut playing cards, since there were none to be found in the building. In fact, there were no blankets or cots, no candles or emergency supplies. No provisions for such a weather emergency had been made at the Center. People slept wherever they could find a comfortable, relatively warm spot, and helped themselves to food in the cafeteria. Detailed records were kept of how much food was eaten and by whom, so the accounts could all be settled when the storm was over.

*The great blizzard of January, 1975, buried dozens of vehicles and stranded 30 people at the EDC for nearly three days.*

*"There were cars stuck from the building all the way out to the cemetery. I was lucky; I was a computer operator at that time, so I kept the computers running, and had something to do to pass the time. I even slept beside the computers! That was in the days of punch cards, and I remember folks getting blank ones from me, writing on them, and making decks of playing cards. Some people volunteered to cook — they had the grill going because I can remember eating hamburgers."*

— Bob Van Den Oever

The refugees from the Blizzard of '75 were snowed in from Friday afternoon until late on Sunday, January 17, when the roads were cleared and help from the outside finally arrived. The ordeal was a lesson to everyone, especially Al Watkins and others in the administration who had never experienced a prairie blizzard firsthand. From that weekend on, the Center was well-stocked with emergency provisions and supplies. The EDC would never be caught unprepared again.

One week after the blizzard buried the Dakota plains in snow, ERTS–2, a twin of the ERTS–1 satellite, was successfully launched from Vandenberg Air Force Base on January 22, 1975. For a variety of reasons, NASA had decided to change the name of the satellites, and from this point on, ERTS became known as Landsat.

With Landsats 1 and 2 now in orbit, the amount of data flowing into the Center was nearly doubled. And the popularity of that data

*Early Landsat images revealed fault lines and other previously unknown geologic features of the Earth's surface.*

was growing worldwide. Additional ground stations for receiving the data were going up in Zaire, Italy and Iran. Remotely sensed satellite imagery was proving to be enormously useful for flood mapping, crop production analyses, mineral, oil and gas exploration, earthquake fault detection, strip mine monitoring, navigation, map-making and a host of other applications.

Yet just as industry and government agencies were getting their first real taste of how the data could be used, the Ford Administration threatened to kill the EROS Program. The White House's Office of Management and Budget suggested that in order to curb federal spending, the EROS Program should be terminated now that Landsat–2 was in orbit. This recommendation also stemmed in part from the defense intelligence community, where some members still were concerned about making global satellite imagery available to anyone or any country around the globe.

Following the tradition set years earlier by Senator Mundt and Congressman Reifel, South Dakota's allies on Capitol Hill came to the rescue of the nation's fledgling civilian land remote sensing program. In response to the OMB's action, Senator James Abourezk and Congressman Larry Pressler introduced legislation to reinstate funding for Landsat. Their request did not go unnoticed. Ford overruled his White House advisors a few months later, and restored the program's budget.

In March, 1975, Glenn Landis, who had been in charge of the Data Production Branch since

Watkins' arrival, became Deputy Chief of the Center. Watkins and Landis would work side by side for the next 16 years. Although very different in their administrative styles, the two men made an effective team and complimented each other's efforts. Watkins tended to be focused on the EDC's dealings with the "outside" world, while Landis managed every detail of the Center's inner workings.

*"Watkins was the one who made sure it stayed, and Landis was the one who made sure it worked."*

— Rita Tornow

*"Those two were kind of interesting to work for because Watkins was kind of free-wheeling, 'let's have fun,' 'be aggressive and creative,' while Landis was a more conserva-tive, 'let's be sure we're doing this right,' go-slow kind of guy. Most of the time, though, they complimented each other quite well. Glenn had the ability to bring reality to many of Watkins' dreams."*

— Wayne Rohde

As Landsat satellite imagery grew in pop-ularity, production in the Photo Lab soared. To handle the increased demand, the Lab acquired new equipment to make the job of image repro-duction easier and more efficient. Several huge photo processing machines, designed and built to EDC specifications, were brought in to make extra-large color prints. State-of-the-art microfilm cameras were added to create both black-and-white and color microfilm of archived images.

*"With our design and fabrication facility here we made major and unique changes to equip-ment. And if there wasn't a machine that did what we wanted it to do, we built it."*

— Bill Happel

The Photo Lab also took innovative steps to recover and recycle many of the chemicals used in its photo processing operation, as well as the silver that was produced as a byproduct. Fifteen to twenty pounds of silver were recovered each month by the Lab, with the help of a computer-

*Judy Collins (left) and Don Becker pass film to be processed through turnstiles in the Photo Lab.*

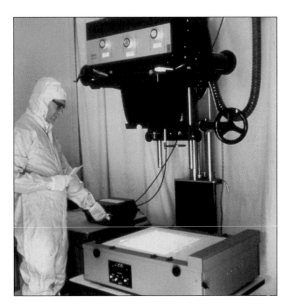

*Bill Winn works at a photo enlarger.*

*Diane Matzke monitors the printing of a large-scale color print.*

*Chuck Luden examines silver recovered from photo processing at the EDC.*

automated recovery system. At the time, the EDC had one of the most advanced chemical recovery and photo lab effluent control systems in the United States.

*"Back in those days, we did a lot of things that vendors...said we couldn't do. We were a test-bed; we had to prove that we could do things to reduce the effluence to the outside, and to regenerate as much as possible to reduce our costs. [People] said there were a lot of things that couldn't be done, but we did them anyway."*

— Brent Nelson

A major highlight for the Computer Services Branch during these years of expansion was the acquisition of the Burroughs 6700 computer system. The Burroughs was a hulking mainframe computer that, when it was installed in

1976, took up two-thirds of the Center's computer room. Its arrival gave the EDC another claim to fame: it was now home to one of the largest computer systems in the Midwest.

*The Burroughs 6700 computer, shortly after it was installed in the Computer Room*

*"We went from a small system to this large mainframe.... [We used it] to keep track of all our satellite images and all our customers and the products they ordered, and to account for the money, but we were also developing things that nobody else we knew had ever developed in the way of software."*
— R.J. Thompson

Software development became a growing focus of the Computer Services Branch, and much of that software was for image processing. For several years, the satellite data that the Center had been receiving from Goddard was in the form of an already processed film product. There were limitations as to what could be done photographically to tailor that product to fit the needs of customers. In the Computer Services Branch, the staff began to design software that would allow the Center to receive data in digital form, and then manipulate it in different ways to produce a wide variety of improved products.

Within the Branch, the staff experimented with a system called EDIES — the EROS Digital Image Enhancement System. The EDIES project was initiated by the Systems Development Branch with both the Applications Branch and the Computer Branch assisting in its design and development, and the Photo Lab assisting in

converting digits to photographic images. EDIES used some software that was developed for the Burroughs 6700 and a number of other computer systems. It was another example of a "do-it-yourself" project since there was no product available to do the job it was hoped EDIES would do.

EDIES was essentially a prototype for the $3.2 million advanced data processing system that was eventually acquired from TRW, Inc., an aerospace development company, in the late 1970s. That system, the EROS Digital Image Processing System, or EDIPS, was designed to interface with NASA computers and allow the Center to receive satellite data in an electronic form that later could be converted into images.

*"By the late 1970s, we were processing digital images, even though most of the rest of the world still wanted photographic products."*
— R.J. Thompson

With the tremendous increase in computing power provided by the Burroughs 6700, the EDC also was able to develop a comprehensive business software system tailored to the Center's unique requirements. The system was dubbed INORAC, for INquiry, ORder, and ACcounting. In an era when prepackaged, off-the-shelf software programs weren't available, INORAC allowed tracking of repeat customers, standing accounts, orders and payments. It also consolidated orders into production-friendly tasks for the Photo Lab and Computer Branch, and even printed order summaries and shipping labels ready to be used in sending out finished products! INORAC was a completely integrated software system for handling the data production business of the Center and it continued in use for many years.

*The User Services Branch, as it looked in the mid-1970s*

*A steady stream of aerial photographs and satellite images make their way through production.*

*"Prior to INORAC, records for everything were kept by hand. It was the first fully automated accounting system here, implemented on the Burroughs 6700 in February, 1977. It was ...pretty state-of-the-art for its day. It also tied together all the Mapping Centers, so that any office could order products from the EDC."*
— Ron Parsons

Within the Applications Branch, many of the science staff were focusing their research on the computerized analysis of remotely sensed data. Fred Waltz was a driving force in setting up an early hub of data analysis and interpretation in the Center known as the Data Analysis Lab, or

*Bonnie (Knuteson) Jenkins prepares images for distribution to EDC customers.*

DAL. The DAL was located in the middle of the building, next to the main computer room. It was a state-of-the-art research center used to develop and demonstrate new capabilities in digital image analysis and processing, and to support training and technical assistance. No other federal institution had anything like it.

Image processing had become a real buzzword in the remote sensing field by the mid 1970's, and the DAL was home to several different systems that could be used to manipulate satellite image data in various ways. One of the first of these systems, the $I^2S$ (I-squared-S) — which was built by a small electronics firm in Kansas — allowed users to scan negative or positive images, as well as Landsat film chips, into a computer using a device resembling a television camera. Once the image was scanned, it could then be manipulated to make color composite images of the Earth's land surfaces.

There was a touch of irony about the process. The film chips had been created at the Goddard Space Flight Center using the digital numbers derived from the sensor aboard the Landsat satellite to modulate an electron beam recorder which, in turn, exposed the film. In using the $I^2S$, EDC scientists essentially reversed the

process — they recreated the digits when they scanned the film.

*"Most of the Landsat data came to us [at that time] on little 70 mm film chips. There was one chip for each band. They looked like a film negative you'd get at any photo processing store, except they were bigger.... We used the $I^2S$ system to scan in these little film chips and register them so we could make a color composite on the screen."*
— Charlie Trautwein

The $I^2S$ image processing system was replaced by the Image 100, a system built by General Electric Company that could read images off magnetic tapes. The Image 100 allowed scientists to carry out a process called "spectral signature classification." In this process, scientists analyzed the digital brightness values in the spectral bands for each individual picture element, or pixel, in a Landsat scene. Then they grouped pixels with similar spectral characteristics into specific "classes" to represent different types of ground features, such as bare ground, grassland, dense forest, standing water, and so forth. Thus, the Image 100 allowed scien-

*The Data Analysis Lab*

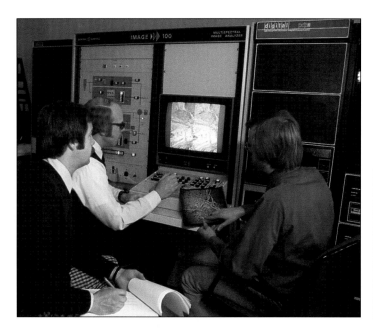

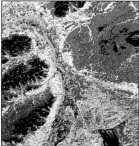

*EDC scientists use the Image 100 (left) to classify various types of surface features by grouping pixels on a satellite image that share similar spectral characteristics (right).*

tists to carry out limited numbers and types of pre-programmed analyses of ground cover in satellite images.

The image processing tool that truly revolutionized satellite data analysis at the EDC, however, was IDIMS, the Interactive Digital Image Manipulation System. IDIMS was an "off-the-shelf" software system built by a small California firm called ESL. It appeared on the scene in the late 1970s, and remained in use at the Center for at least a decade. Unlike the Image 100, IDIMS was a very interactive system for which scientists could write programs that would instruct the computer to manipulate satellite image data in unique ways. Being programmable, IDIMS was a flexible processing system, and a significant improvement over any of its predecessors. Very quickly, IDIMS became the core of the DAL.

*"[IDIMS] was a turning point because it changed the environment here. The systems we'd had before, there were very few around, and so there were very few people you could contact 'out there' who were using the same system.... But IDIMS...was a system that was resold many times, and so a group of IDIMS users was formed, and that became a real [source of] technical exchange."*

— June Thormodsgard

Training programs were another major focus in the Applications Branch. Formal training classes in the interpretation and application of remotely sensed images had begun in the Downtown Office, under Don Kulow's enthusiastic direction, after it became clear that educating potential users about Landsat data and encouraging its wider use were essential in order to derive the greatest benefits from this new technology. The Applications Branch continued this effort on a much larger scale by

*Brian Berg operates IDIMS, the Interactive Digital Image Manipulation System.*

*Don Orr lectures to a domestic training class.*

setting up extensive training programs in the use of remotely sensed data. Training was handled by the Training and Assistance Section of the Branch, initially headed by Don Lauer and, later, Bill Draeger.

*"Our mission...was very clear. Find mechanisms to maximize the use of aerial photography and satellite remote sensing within the operational bureaus of the DOI, so they would improve the efficiency of their job managing national parks, the nation's range lands, the fish and wildlife resources of the country — that was our charge."*
— Don Lauer

The main thrust of the Training and Assistance Sections's efforts was in working with various federal agencies within the Department of the Interior. Initially, many of these "domestic" training courses consisted of one- or two-week workshops that were tailor-made to fit the remote sensing needs of a particular agency. In these courses, ecologists, geologists, hydrologists, land use planners, and

resource managers usually came to the EDC to learn how to interpret remotely sensed data and how it could be applied in their work. The goal was one of "technology transfer" — once these various agencies became familiar with satellite images and remote sensing technology, it was hoped they would continue to use these new tools on their own.

*"We really put together the first intensive 'soup to nuts' remote sensing training courses in the country."*
— Dennis Hood

Some of the training courses were standard classroom experiences. In other cases, scientists and resource managers came to the Center for less formal, but more intense "technical assistance" interactions, in which they worked closely with members of the EDC staff for several days or weeks, primarily in the Data Analysis Lab, to learn a specific aspect of remote sensing technology or experiment with digital image processing as it related to a specific problem or project.

*"In the DAL is where our visiting scientists would get hooked!"*

— June Thormodsgard

But perhaps the most effective training strategy used by the Applications Branch was the setting up of demonstration, or cooperative, projects. A truly hands-on approach to training, cooperative projects were joint research efforts in which EDC staff worked with staff from a federal agency to help solve actual environmental or resource management problems using satellite images and aerial photography. The Center staff provided technical support in developing and carrying out these projects. When the projects were finished, the agency participants had not only gained a working knowledge of remote sensing technology, but they had first-hand experience in demonstrating its value in a real-life situation.

One of the first cooperative projects undertaken by the EDC was with the Bureau of Land Management (BLM) in Alaska, specifically 2.5 million acres in Denali National Park. This was a pilot program designed to demonstrate how Landsat imagery could be used to classify vegetation in a wilderness environment.

Initially, BLM land managers came to the EDC where they learned the basics of data interpretation and then worked in the DAL to process satellite images of the Denali area in such a way as to distinguish various types of vegetation. The land managers, however, were somewhat skeptical as to the accuracy of the data that had been derived.

So in order to prove their point, EDC researchers accompanied BLM participants back to Alaska, where they selected a random sampling of 1-acre field plots in the study area. After identifying the plots from the air, five field crews consisting of representatives from BLM, the EDC, and several Alaskan land resource agencies were then flown into these wilderness areas by helicopter. They would hike through each plot, record the vegetation and terrain conditions there, and compare what they found to the vegetation information that had been derived from the Landsat imagery.

It took about a half day to map the vegetation in each plot. Most of these locations were deep in the heart of the Alaskan wilderness, where it was easy to be surprised by some of the larger native wildlife. Grizzly bears were always a concern on these excursions into the remote regions of Denali.

*Mapping the vegetation of field plots in the wilds of Denali National Park, Alaska*

*"We never had any actual run-ins with bears. But once, after the pilot dropped us off in a plot, he noticed a grizzly on a ridge about a mile from where we were, heading in our direction. He tried to scare the bear off with the helicopter, and he must have been successful because we never saw it. But the pilot was on the verge of coming back to get us...."*

— Wayne Rohde

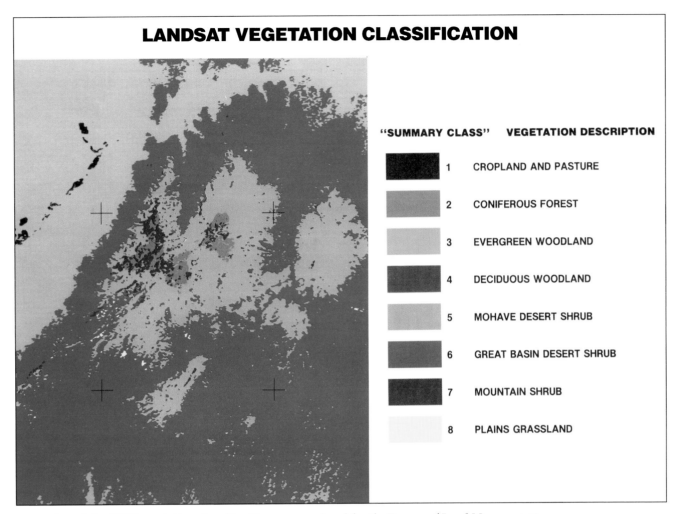

*A portion of the AVRI vegetation classification map produced for the Bureau of Land Management*

The results of the field testing clearly demonstrated that it was possible to classify vegetation using satellite images. There was considerable room for improvement in the process, but the EDC researchers had made their point.

The interaction with BLM continued with a second cooperative project called the Arizona Vegetation Resource Inventory (AVRI). BLM managers wanted to inventory the different kinds of vegetation in the states bordering the Colorado River — a huge area in which, like Alaska, assessing natural resources from the ground was virtually impossible. Using the lessons learned in Alaska, EDC researchers again worked with BLM staff to use Landsat imagery to classify and map vegetation throughout this vast chunk of the American west. This time, however, they also included elevation data in their classification scheme, a strategy that greatly improved the accuracy of the results.

*"AVRI was a significant breakthrough in the transferring of remote sensing technology to a federal user agency. With EDC playing the role of an intermediary, we demonstrated to the BLM how digital satellite imagery could be used as a tool in support of their resource management responsibilities. After AVRI, the BLM went on to establish similar projects on their own, without EDC's assistance."*
— Wayne Miller

EDC scientists then took the AVRI project one step further — they applied the information about vegetation that had been obtained through image processing to solve a practical, real-life problem facing the BLM. The agency wanted to transplant big horn sheep into the area, and needed to know where the most suitable big horn sheep habitat was to be found. Rising to the challenge, the EDC team searched the data base they had created to pinpoint areas with the specific environmental characteristics needed by big horn sheep, including vegetation, elevation, steepness and direction of slope, distance from roads, and so forth. They used those criteria to create overlays, and presented BLM with a "map" of the sites where the data indicated transplanted big horn sheep would be most likely to thrive.

After successfully completing the AVRI project, the BLM went on to do a similar project, in Idaho, called IVRI, but with far less involvement on the part of the EDC. This was precisely the outcome Center scientists were working toward. Once an agency got a taste of what remote sensing technology could do, it could set up its own labs, train additional staff, and forge ahead on its own.

Throughout the latter half of the 1970s and into the 1980s, EDC scientists carried out similar cooperative projects with many federal agencies, including the National Park Service, the Bureau of Indian Affairs, the Fish and Wildlife Service, the Bureau of Reclamation, and the Office of Surface Mining. They often took the initiative in setting the projects in motion. After investigating a particular group's needs in resource management or research, they would approach that group with an idea for working together. The cooperative project approach was enormously successful in getting federal agencies to use remotely sensed imagery. And while the EDC gradually worked itself out of a job in the cooperative project arena, it also created a large user group, and an ever-expanding market for Landsat data.

*"To sell ourselves, we would do a little bit of their project on our own, with our own money, and take it to them and say 'Now look at this — if you did this and this, or if we helped you to continue with this, here are some of the benefits you'd get from it.' They would see it firsthand, and...we'd hook 'em!"*

— Jim Sturdevant

Transferring remote sensing technology to user groups in the United States was the first priority of the Training and Assistance Section at

the EDC. But another important focus of the training program was on the international community. Landsats 1 and 2 were orbiting the Earth roughly every hour and a half, taking pictures of the entire planet, not just the continental United States. That emerging global data set was an untapped resource waiting to be exploited.

*"This robust global data started to become available and there was a crying need for it internationally. Research managers and planners in other countries could see the potential of the data, but they didn't know much about it, they didn't understand its characteristics, and they didn't know how to use it."*

— Don Lauer

International remote sensing training courses were held twice a year at the EDC, in the spring and fall. Each course lasted roughly a month. During the first two weeks of the course, the thirty or so participants were introduced to the basics of photo interpretation and satellite imagery, and taught how manually to analyze remotely sensed images, most of which were of the state of South Dakota. During the third week, the group went on a field trip to the Black Hills and applied what they had learned along the way. The field analyses helped the students correlate features on the ground with what they had seen in aerial photographs or satellite imagery.

*"We'd have a week or two of lectures and exercises, an academic approach. Then there would be a field trip. South Dakota is tailor-made for that because if you go from here to Deadwood, you hit it all: agricultural land, range land, an arid environment — the Badlands — and a mountainous forest area — the Black Hills."*

— Ron Beck

During the final week of the international course, the students, armed with aerial photographs and satellite imagery of their respective countries, designed projects in which remote sensing technology was utilized to

*Students from all over the world attend one of the EDC international training courses in remote sensing and its applications.*

*Ron Beck (left) explains an aspect of image interpretation to a group of international students.*

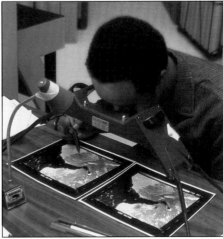

*Using a stereoscope to view Landsat images*

*International students compare satellite imagery to their surroundings in the Black Hills of South Dakota.*

address real natural resource or land management problems they were facing back home.

The international courses attracted students from all over the world. In one row of the classroom there might be scientists from Australia, Iran, Malaysia, Saudi Arabia, Israel, and Argentina. The cultural exchange was an added bonus of these courses, although not always a predictable one.

*"We had a man from Sweden who, within two weeks, met the love of his life, and actually came back...to marry her, and take her back to Stockholm. And I spent a fair amount of time over the years in the Deadwood police station, getting some of our students out of jail for various minor offenses."*

— Ron Beck

In the late 1970s, a number of international courses were also held on foreign soil, in Argentina and Iran. The purpose of these workshops was to train Argentineans and Iranians how to plan and put on remote sensing training programs, and assemble and educate their own teams of remote sensing experts.

*East meets the "real" West on a field trip to the Badlands. (Left: Ron Beck)*

*"I took a crash course in Spanish before I went down to Argentina the first time, but when I got down there, they wouldn't let me speak any Spanish because they all wanted to practice their English! Instruction in the workshops was in English. If they needed any translation, they would do it for me because [when I tried] I would bumble through it and be so slow that they'd get impatient."*

— Charlie Trautwein

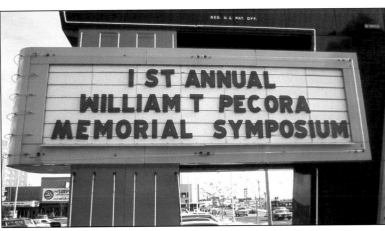

*The marquee at the downtown Holiday Inn in Sioux Falls advertises the first Pecora Conference in the fall of 1975.*

Through its national and international training courses the EDC went a long way toward establishing the worldwide market for remotely sensed land surface data. The international programs, in particular, gave the Center exposure on nearly every continent. It wasn't long before the EDC came to be regarded as a model for what a "data center" should be, and as a result, it was visited by representatives from many foreign countries who wanted to observe first hand how the EDC did business. In numerous cases, these visitors returned to their homelands and supervised the building of facilities that were closely modeled after the EDC. This high level of international visibility, and credibility, continues today.

*"A lot of visitors, especially from the international scientific community, would come here and tour the Photo Lab. It was a showplace and a training ground, where we trained foreigners because of the unique work we did with Landsat data and aerial photography."*

— Bill Happel

It was in this same spirit of international cooperation and collaboration that the Center instituted the William T. Pecora Memorial Symposia in the mid-1970s. These multi-day conferences brought together hundreds of government, industry and university scientists from around the world to foster an exchange of scientific and resource management findings resulting from the use of remotely sensed data. The theme for the first Pecora Symposium, which was held in October, 1975, revolved around how satellite data could be used to aid in the global search for fuel and mineral deposits. The Pecora Symposia have remained regular events at the EDC ever since.

On March 5, 1978, Landsat–3 soared into orbit carrying an advanced version of the MSS sensor. The EROS Data Center seemed to be soaring, too. In just a few years, the Center had evolved from a photographic reproduction facility into an advanced data processing laboratory with an international reputation. But clouds were gathering on the horizon, and events were about to transpire that would cast a shadow over the EDC and its endeavors for some time to come.

# – 10 –
# Clouds Over EROS (1979-1984)

In 1979, President Jimmy Carter issued a presidential directive that called for a number of changes to be made in the Landsat satellite program. The directive proposed initially transferring the responsibility for Landsat operations from NASA to the National Oceanographic and Atmospheric Administration (NOAA), an agency of the Department of Commerce. It recommended that four additional satellites be developed in the coming years. And — most significantly — Carter's directive also recommended that the operation of the satellites, and the control and distribution of the data they generated, be gradually turned over to the private sector in the next ten years. In a word, the Landsat program was to become commercialized.

The call for commercialization of Landsat grew out of the idea that by turning over the program to private industry, the government would save money, and at the same time, allow the satellite data industry to develop in a free market economy. Yet there were many people involved with the Landsat program who felt that such a move was decidedly premature.

Carter's directive raised a troubling question for those at the EROS Data Center: If private industry took over the production and distribution of Landsat satellite data, what, if any, role would the EDC continue to play in the program? A cloud of uncertainty was cast over the Center, and the EROS Program in general. Everyone recognized that there would be changes coming if, indeed, the Landsat program were commercialized. Yet at this point in time, it was difficult to predict what those changes might be, or their full impact on the Center and its employees. While Carter's proposal was mulled over in

*The DOMSAT antenna goes up on the snowy grounds outside the EDC.*

*The DOMSAT receiving link, inside the Center*

government circles and discussed among top administrators at the EDC, the Center staff for the most part forged ahead with their work, and poured their energy into continuing the creative efforts begun in the previous few years, in research, training, processing, distributing and archiving remotely sensed land data.

The final year of the decade was a busy, somewhat tumultuous one at the EDC. It began with the installation of a 30-foot antenna on the grounds in front of the Center. Known as the DOMSAT antenna, the huge dish made it possible for the EDC to receive Landsat MSS data, in digital form, directly from Goddard Space Flight Center in Maryland via a domestic communications satellite orbiting in space. The antenna became operational in May of 1979, and was a milestone in the Center's history, because although there was still no direct link between the EDC and a Landsat satellite, there was now at least a direct link to Goddard. Gone were the days of receiving film and computer tapes by mail or commercial aircraft from the East Coast.

The link to Goddard improved both the quality of and the speed at which satellite data reached the Center. That, in turn, reduced data processing time from weeks to days.

About the same time as the antenna was going up, construction began on a major conservation project just behind the building. Splayed out on a huge slab of concrete was a dazzling array of solar panels, 10,000 square feet of them, all lined up in neat rows and tilted toward the southern sky. Interest in solar power, and other renewable energy sources, was keen at this point in the nation's history, as a result of oil embargoes, fuel shortages and skyrocketing prices for oil, gasoline and natural gas. When the Center had been built in the early 1970s, heating oil was selling for 13 cents a gallon. Now in the face of the "energy crunch," the price had jumped to nearly a dollar a gallon. Energy conservation quickly became a major issue at the EDC, as it did all across the country.

The Photo Lab used 20,000 gallons of hot water every day in its film processing activities. Fuel oil was burned to heat that water, and as the price of fuel oil soared, the staff began to explore more cost-effective — and environmentally friendly — alternatives. Funding to erect the solar collector came in the form of a $500,000 grant from the Department of Energy, part of a federal program aimed at building "demonstration projects" that would test the effectiveness and economics of solar power applications. The solar panel array was designed by the engineering and architectural firm of Spitznagel Partners, Inc. When the massive solar collector was completed in early 1980, it became one of the largest solar water heating systems in the country. It reduced the Center's dependence on fuel oil and saved a considerable amount of money each year. As a result of other creative efforts, energy consumption was reduced dramatically elsewhere in the Center. One good example was the heat recovery system — designed and installed by employees of Viking Engineering Services, Inc. (Vesco), the building engineering and maintenance contractor — that captured waste heat coming off the computers and circulated it around the building as supplemental heat.

*Construction on the solar collector began in 1979; it was completed in 1980.*

*"We were mandated to reduce energy consumption by 20%. We ended up reducing it by 37%. With the heat recovery system, we were able to heat the whole building with the heat recovered from the computers — the thermostats were set at 65 degrees, but it was 72 degrees in the building because we were using that waste heat."*

— Robin Hermanson

Skyrocketing fuel costs also led to the creation of a ride-share program at the EDC, an endeavor which was immediately successful, and which continues to this day. The project began in 1979 when several EDC employees, under the direction of Woody Yaroch, then Chief of the Administrative Branch, applied for a loan from the Federal Highway Administration to start a vanpool program. When the group learned that the loans could only be made to non-federal entities, Mayor Rick Knobe volunteered the city of Sioux Falls as the "middleman" for a loan pass-through.

The employees incorporated themselves as The EROS Vanpooling Association, a not-for-profit corporation, and subsequently secured the funding to purchase four vans. The vanpool eventually grew to include seven vans servicing the Sioux Falls, Brandon, and Dell Rapids areas, with a vanpool membership of over 90 participants. The cost to each vanpool member was (and still is) roughly $35 a month for door-to-door service to and from the Center. Not only does the vanpool save an estimated 15,000 gallons of gasoline a year, but it also provides a certain peace of mind that comes from traveling with a group on country roads during South Dakota's often perilous winters.

*EDC employees head toward the fleet of Vanpool vehicles at the end of a work day.*

*"It saves money, it's relaxing, and I enjoy being in the van with people from other departments. It's always been a good way to get to know people really well. In the winter, you don't have to worry about driving on icy roads...you get picked up at your door and that's hard to beat!"*

— Linda Hansen,
vanpool member since 1979

On June 25, 1979, the EDC experienced the first and only serious labor dispute in its history. About a dozen Vesco employees walked off their jobs that day to protest what they believed were unfair wage practices and working conditions. After two picket lines went up, another thirty Vesco and sixty Technicolor Graphics Services employees — primarily electricians, plumbers and Photo Lab employees, all of whom belonged to the same AFL-CIO union as the strikers — refused to cross the picket lines. Some of the sympathizers also joined the picketers.

*"We felt we had no choice. We were actually trying to help out another union, by honoring their strike — we would not cross their picket lines. We were up pretty late that night, trying to decide what to do...."*

— Diane Matzke

Vesco hired replacements for the maintenance workers who had walked off their jobs. But the sympathy strike and the picketing continued, all the while receiving considerable coverage in the local press. When it became obvious after a few days that contract negotiations were at a standstill and that there was no hope for a quick res-

olution, staff members from other branches of the EDC were temporarily assigned to the Photo Lab to continue the work of those who were out on the picket lines. Within three weeks, however, the dispute ended with the help of federal mediators. Employees on the picket lines returned to their jobs at the Center, and by the end of the summer, most members of the original group of Vesco employees who had lost their jobs at the outset of the strike were rehired.

*Janice King (left) and Chester Thompson picket outside the Data Center.*

**Clouds Over EROS (1979-1984)**

In light of its continually expanding archive of Earth images, it was natural that the Center should become involved in the National High Altitude Photography Program (NHAP) — later renamed the National Aerial Photography Program (NAPP) — at this point in its history. Aerial photography had long played a critically important role in the work of many federal agencies, from the map-making efforts of the USGS, to crop acreage compliance programs of the Department of Agriculture, to natural resource surveys by the Bureau of Land Management, the Fish and Wildlife Service, and others. Yet for many years, each agency operated

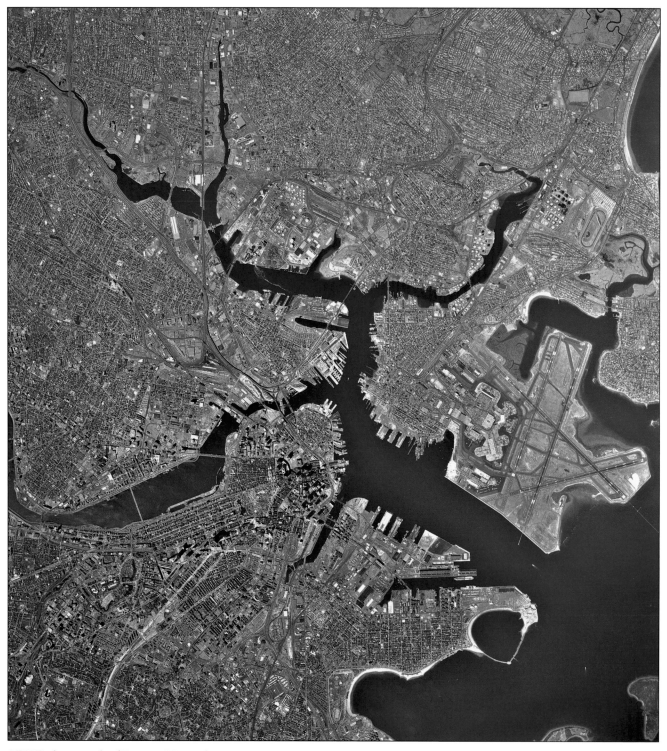

*NHAP photograph of Boston, Massachusetts*

its own aerial photography program, designed to meet its particular needs, without much regard as to what other agencies were acquiring in the way of high altitude photos. The result was that different agencies often flew over the same areas of land, each taking their own pictures in different photographic formats. It was a wasteful approach, one that by the late 1970s was ripe for change.

The solution to the problem was NHAP, a coordinated, standardized program designed to acquire aerial photography of the United States in a very systematic way. EDC staff were involved in organizing NHAP from its earliest beginnings. Under the program, various federal agencies pooled their resources and the USGS assumed responsibility for acquiring both black-and-white and color-infrared photographic images of the conterminous United States. The first NHAP flights began in 1980, with plans to repeat the process and update the complete aerial photographic record of the forty-eight States approximately every five years.

The NHAP Program was an immediate success. The aerial photos were exceptionally clear, revealing minute details about the Earth's land surface from 40,000 feet up. NHAP data quickly became a major product line for the Center. Furthermore, the EDC became the archival repository for all those NHAP (later NAPP) photos, and continues in that role.

*"NHAP was regarded as a model of coopera-tion between the competing agencies, having minimized duplication of aerial photography."*
— Glenn Landis

A major undertaking was launched in the Applications Branch in late 1979, partly as a result of a change in the directorship at the USGS. Bill Menard, selected by the Carter Administration to direct the Geological Survey, felt that the agency needed a stronger presence in Alaska, a state that contained vast, relatively uncharted natural resources. Menard invited proposals for ways in which to accomplish this goal. Don Lauer, Don Orr and others in the Applications Branch responded with the sugges-tion that the EDC set up a Field Office in Anchorage, where most of the state and federal

land management agencies in Alaska were located. Having a Field Office in Anchorage would not only give the EDC a presence in Alaska, but it would make it easier for EDC researchers to further the transfer of remote sensing technology, and its applications, to the Alaskan resource management community.

*"And so we put in a proposal to extend the things we do in Sioux Falls at the EDC into Alaska...by setting up a Field Office... creating, in a sense, a micro-EDC. It would be very small, but very focused on Alaska."*
— Don Lauer

Menard was enthusiastic about the idea, and Dave Carneggie was given the job of setting up the Alaska Field Office. While a suitable building in Anchorage was found and refitted, Carneggie went about procuring an IDIMS system for the Office, which would become the centerpiece of the operations there. Establishing the Field Office was another example of the EDC's doing "whatever was required" in action. There were no guidelines to follow in setting up such a facility, just a sense of determination, creativity, and enthusiasm on the part of the fledgling Field Office staff.

The Alaska Field Office opened in the spring of 1980, with Carneggie as government manager, and Mark Shasby as the contractor supervisor. As soon as the IDIMS system was up and running, members of the Alaskan offices of the Bureau of Land Management, the Fish and Wildlife Service, the National Park Service, and other agencies came to see what IDIMS could do. The agencies had a pressing need to learn the new technology, because Congress had recently passed the Alaska National Interest Lands Conservation Act (ANILCA), which mandated that all major land management agen-cies in Alaska inventory the state's resources — from vegetation cover and wildlife habitat to archeological sites — within a very tight time frame. The Act put an enormous amount of pres-sure on the Department of the Interior's agen-cies. In a huge state with almost no roads and very few airports, the only way to accomplish such a task was to use remote sensing. Many of the resource agencies in Alaska quickly entered into cooperative projects with the Alaska Field Office to use Landsat data to carry out the daunting task with which they had been charged.

In some respects the Alaska Field Office was a remote outpost. But those who worked there had access to the last great frontier in North America. Whenever an opportunity came along for EDC staff to spend time up at the Field Office, they usually jumped at the chance.

*"Needless to say, everyone...in the Alaska Field Office had the opportunity to go out into uncharted areas in Alaska, using planes or whatever kinds of equipment that could take you to places that few people have been. Whenever we would come here to give briefings, as much as hearing about the professional activities, people really wanted to hear about the experiences the staff was having each time they'd go out into the wilds to do field work."*
— Dave Carneggie

Back "home" at the EDC, major developments were taking place in the area of satellite image processing. EDIPS, the EROS Digital Image Processing System, had been up and running since 1979, and would remain the Center's standard data production system for the next 17 years. EDIPS provided the EDC with fast, efficient data processing capabilities for Landsat MSS data recorded on high density tapes.

EDIPS would extract image data from the tapes and then computer-enhance those data to improve overall quality by removing electronic "noise" and the effects of atmospheric haze, thus increasing the contrast and sharpening fine details. Those resulting images were then transferred onto film using high resolution laser film recording equipment. Producing large quantities of enhanced satellite imagery from digital tapes was something few organizations were capable of at the time.

As the months passed, however, it became evident that it would be advantageous to establish a core group of people at the Center who could devote their time to working exclusively on producing new types of standardized products from digital data. The group started small, with two or three computer scientists in the Computer Services Branch who were charged with this task. For a time, this arrangement

*The EDC's Alaska Field Office in Anchorage*

*Digital image of Mt. McKinley and the Alaska Range, near Denali National Park*

*EDIPS, the EROS Digital Image Processing System (upper left), occupied a prominent place in the Computer Room in the late 1970s.*

worked out quite nicely, but eventually that small cadre was moved into the Data Services Branch where it became known as the Digital Data Production Section. The DDPS was responsible for creating specially enhanced images on demand to satisfy the needs of various government agencies.

At the same time, the scientists within the Applications Branch were developing a host of new applications, many of which resulted from cooperative projects with other federal agencies. As these projects grew in scope, the amount of processing that was required to produce various types of digital products also grew. There were commonalities in the processing requirements. For example, scientists often wanted multiple images to be mosaicked together to form an image of a large area, or they needed images merged with other data sets. Image mapping — combining photographic images of land surfaces with geographic attributes such as lines of latitude and longitude or boundaries of coun-

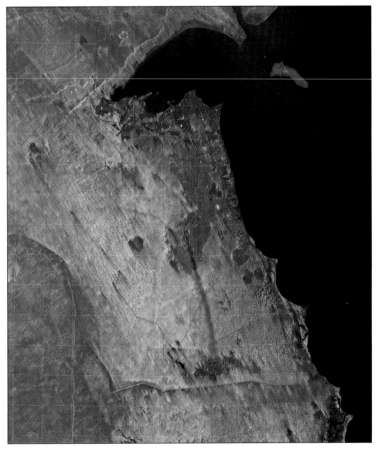

*An image map of Kuwait*

*EDC scientists at work on RIPS*

tries — was another area in which the creative expertise of the Digital Data Production lab came to the fore. Much of what came to be regarded as "standard" digital data production became the responsibility of the Digital Data Production Section as time went on.

*"So rather than have the SAB scientists do that [kind of processing] themselves, we decided to create that capability in our Data Services Branch and put that standard digital data production requirement in one place. In time, the Digital Data Production Section really grew, and the SAB came to rely heavily on them for support."*

— Wayne Rohde

Within the Applications Branch, research on image processing was proceeding along many lines as well. A new computer system known as RIPS was developed; the acronym stood for Remote Image Processing System. RIPS was among the first portable computer systems that could be used for digital image processing. Up until that time, spectral signature classification of Landsat images was something that could only be accomplished in large, sophisticated computer laboratories. RIPS made it possible for researchers to use small computers in field office settings to perform many of the same image-classification tasks. RIPS could be interfaced with many different kinds of host computers, which made it a very flexible, versatile system. It quickly became an invaluable tool for both research applications and training.

*"After RIPS was developed we brought it into these remote sensing workshops that we were giving, and used it as the main tool for training people how to process remote sensing data digitally."*

— Charlie Trautwein

EDC scientists were also beginning to experiment with the relatively new technology of Geographic Information Systems (GIS). A GIS is a computerized information system that can be used to manipulate and analyze geographically, or "spatially," referenced data. In a GIS, different types of data bases are merged to answer questions about geography, natural resources, and especially the relationships that exist between different aspects of a geographic area. For example, by combining a data base that contains information on soil types, drainage systems, waterways, and transportation routes with a satellite image of a given area, an image map can be created that reveals the complex relationships that exist among those various elements.

*"We...broadened our perspectives to focus beyond just the image data and how you extract information from images. We went into the new and evolving computer mapping area of geographic information systems. We very aggressively pursued that from a research standpoint and it proved to be a wonderful move on our part."*

— Don Lauer

When the USGS management was initially getting interested in GIS

technology, they turned to the EDC for assistance in understanding how GIS might be applied to the Survey's projects. Within the Center's Applications Branch, scientists set up a hypothetical project designed to demonstrate to headquarters just what a geographic information system could do. The project was called the Federal Mineral Land Information System (FMLIS) and it was designed to answer the question: Where in the United States are mineral resources located on federal lands?

Medford, Oregon, was chosen as the first test case site for the FMLIS project. A computer data base was created that incorporated Bureau of Land Management maps that showed lands owned by various federal agencies in the Medford area, information about types of mineral rights owned by the federal government, USGS minerals maps and other information about mineral resources in Oregon, plus geographic reference information such as roads and county boundaries. When all these data were digitized and organized within a GIS format, the result was displayed as a map showing precisely where in the region around Medford there were mineral deposits located on federal lands.

Once again, EDC staff had done "whatever it

*A GIS image created in the early 1980s shows lead-zinc deposits near Rolla, Missouri. Areas with the highest potential for deposits appear red-orange; white lines show boundaries of already established mining districts in the area.*

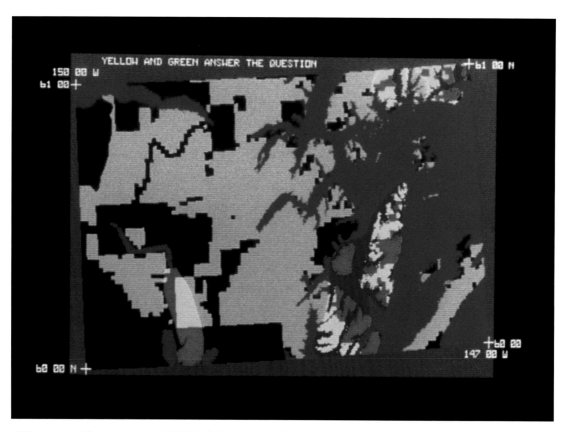

*GIS image of the area around Medford, Oregon, produced as part of the FMLIS project*

took." The results of the FMLIS project were impressive, and were a major factor in prompting the USGS to pursue GIS technology and fund research on its applications.

*"We marched the [FMLIS] results into Headquarters and briefed the USGS Director. He was so taken with it that he said: 'I want to see the whole thing for the state of Alaska!' And so we did the same thing for Alaska. FMLIS really demonstrated the concept of what GIS could do."*

— Jim Sturdevant

While the USGS went on to create its own GIS research labs, EDC scientists continued their own exploration of the technology, especially as to how it could be used with satellite imagery and other types of remotely sensed data. That work continues today.

The early 1980s was a time of rapid change in the area of computer technology and digital image processing. Change often brings strife, and a program called the Land Analysis System (LAS) was one development at the EDC that put

the Applications and Computer Branches at odds for a time. LAS was a cooperative project carried out with software developers at Goddard Space Flight Center. LAS was initially developed for the VAX computer system — which had replaced the Burroughs — and which had become the scientific computer of choice for many at this time. But LAS was also designed to be a "transportable" image processing software system that could be installed on any computer.

At the Center, LAS was promoted primarily by the Computer Branch and was designed to replace the Image 100 and IDIMS systems used by the Applications Branch. IDIMS, in particular, was much beloved by most EDC applications scientists, and they were reluctant to see it go.

*"[LAS] wasn't very interactive, like what all the scientists back here [in Applications] had cut their teeth on. Suddenly we had these black boxes! It almost got to be like armed camps. In this branch we missed IDIMS...."*

— June Thormodsgard

*"The move to replace the Image 100 and IDIMS...immediately put us at odds with the scientists, who were IDIMS gurus."*
— R.J. Thompson

To make matters worse, the Computer Branch then initiated the move to the UNIX operating system. That was a bold move on the part of R.J. Thompson and others in the Branch, because the availability of qualified, tested UNIX systems was still a few years down the road. All told, the introduction of LAS and the move to UNIX created considerable controversy between the computer staff and the applications scientists that persisted into the early 1990s.

*"The transportability of UNIX made the selection of future computer platforms more flexible and competitive. R.J. championed the UNIX cause and defended it in the face of considerable resistance. Time has vindicated his position."*
— Glenn Landis

So it was that work continued on many fronts at the EDC during the first half of the 1980s. Great strides were made and much was achieved, but behind the technological advances, the threat of Landsat's commercialization was looming, like a gathering storm.

When President Carter had initially proposed commercializing the Landsat system back in 1979, it was to be a gradual process. The situation changed dramatically when Ronald Reagan took office. In 1981, the Reagan Administration accelerated the pace of Landsat's commercialization, proposing to end government operation of the satellite system by 1985.

The Reagan Administration's eagerness to shed itself of Landsat also reflected changing attitudes about the environment and the need to manage, conserve and protect natural resources. Environmental protection and careful resource management were no longer in vogue. Reagan and his advisors were much more focused on building the nation's military capacities in light of the Cold War than the Carter Administration had been, and a program such as Landsat was

considered fair game to be cut free from government support.

The accelerated push toward commercialization placed the EROS Data Center in a vulnerable position. Its future was no longer assured, since its production and distribution functions were soon to be made obsolete by commercialization. To make matters worse, there had been a 25 percent drop in sales at the Center. Budget cuts led to the laying off of more than a dozen TGS employees in March, 1982. It seemed that even the satellites themselves were reflecting the trouble on the ground during this period; communication had been lost with Landsat–2, and Landsat–3 was beginning to malfunction. The amount of data flowing into the Center was cut in half.

On July 16, 1982, Landsat–4 was successfully launched, a bright moment in these discouraging times. The desperately needed satellite was equipped with a new type of sensor, the Thematic Mapper, which had finer resolution (30 meters) and more spectral bands than any previous Landsat sensor. Landsat–4 beamed down to Earth the clearest, most detailed, and most informative images of the surface of the planet that had ever been taken by a non-military satellite. In those images, it was possible to pick out features about the size of a baseball diamond.

As 1982 came to a close, the EDC became part of the National Mapping Division of the USGS, but the specter of cutbacks and possible closure still seemed unshakable. South Dakota Senator Larry Pressler kept up a running battle with the White House, NASA and various federal agencies to keep the Data Center afloat. From the outset, Pressler had been very critical of the proposal to transfer the Landsat operations to a private corporation, and he worked hard to champion the EDC cause.

Early in 1983, NASA turned over the formal control of the Landsat program to NOAA and the Department of Commerce. One of NOAA's first actions was to raise the price of Landsat data products, a step that reflected the Reagan Administration's decision that user fees must be high enough to cover all costs of operating and maintaining the Landsat system. NOAA also raised the fees paid by each foreign ground station to access Landsat data, from $200,000 to $600,000 annually. No one doubted that these price increases would have a negative impact on Landsat data sales.

As the months passed, the Commerce Department worked to interest private investors in taking over the Landsat satellite program, but with little success. No private corporation had yet shown much enthusiasm in maintaining the program without the benefit of huge government subsidies. Yet a final decision on the commercialization situation was set to be made in early 1984.

*Thematic Mapper image of White Sands, New Mexico*

This is how matters stood when the EDC celebrated its 10th Anniversary in September, 1983. It was an occasion worthy of celebrating considering how far the Center had come in a single decade. Months of preparation went into the gala affair. An open house, complete with slide shows and the unveiling of a six-foot-diameter rotating, geophysical globe, was held on September 24. The highlight of the celebration was an air show featuring acrobatic stunt flying, ultra light planes, skydivers, and hot air balloons. But at a time that seemed to be plagued by trouble, the air show was marred by tragedy. Hundreds of spectators watched as the wings of an ultra light plane folded and the aircraft plunged 800 feet to the ground, killing the pilot on impact.

The following summer, only a few weeks after the successful launch of Landsat–5, Congress passed the Land Remote Sensing Commercialization Act, calling for the private sector takeover of the Landsat system. With that action, the threat of commercialization was realized.

*The poster created by Lee McManus for the Data Center's 10th Anniversary Celebration*

# – 11 –
# An Uncertain Future (1985-1989)

For nearly five years, there had been considerable speculation about the future of the Landsat program. With the passing of the Land Remote Sensing Commercialization Act, that speculation ended and the staff at the EROS Data Center braced themselves for the rapid changes that were about to take place, changes that would have a major impact on the Center's future.

Several months passed as the small group of private corporations vying for Landsat ownership was gradually narrowed to one. On September 27, 1985, the Maryland-based Earth Observation Satellite Company, or EOSAT, was awarded a contract to own and operate the Landsat system for a period of ten years. EOSAT was a joint venture of the RCA Corporation and the Hughes Aircraft Company.

*EOSAT became the commercial operator of the Landsat program in late 1985.*

The terms of the contract called for EOSAT to operate Landsats 4 and 5, and to build two new satellites in a timely fashion to replace them. EOSAT would have exclusive rights to acquire and market all Landsat satellite data collected prior to the 1985 agreement, and similar rights to all subsequent data for ten years from its date of acquisition. The new company would also receive all foreign ground station fees, and several hundred million dollars in government subsidies.

As part of the agreement with EOSAT, the EROS Data Center would continue to receive, process, and distribute Landsat data for a few years, with funding from the Commerce Department, while EOSAT built its own production facilities. But despite the Center's involvement, EOSAT would retain all the revenue from the sales of that data. The new company was free to set data prices at whatever level it saw fit to cover its own costs and make a profit. All in all, the Center stood to lose about $6 million a year as a result of commercialization, roughly one-third of its total operating budget at the time. Furthermore, a fundamental reason for the Center's existence — the processing and distribution of Landsat data — had been stripped away.

> *"We were going to be the Mecca for receiving, processing and distributing Landsat satellite data. Now that was transferred to the private sector. Our mission evaporated on us. And without a mission, you're in deep trouble."*
>
> — Don Lauer

Yet facing challenges was nothing new at the EROS Data Center. Throughout its history there had been setbacks, obstacles to overcome, problems to solve. Although it appeared that the EDC's involvement with the Landsat program was doomed, the attitude reflected in Al Schock's old slogan "Whatever is required, we will do it!" was still alive and well among the staff. Ever since the first concerns about commercialization had been raised in the early 1980s, the Center had begun to gradually diversify its research programs and activities. Now that effort was intensified, and over the next few years the staff poured their energies into developing new applications for remote sensing technology along several fronts.

*"Commercialization forced our hand. We redesigned the Science and Applications Branch to have a much stronger research component. We knew there were going to be new data types available...and we wanted to know what their potential was. We focused... on maximizing the use of these new data sources...to better assess, inventory, and map the land."*

— Don Lauer

In was in this context, then, that around 1986 the Center looked beyond the borders of the United States for new opportunities. Don Moore, a soil chemist who had joined the Applications Branch several years earlier, brought with him considerable experience working in arid parts of Africa. Moore proposed expanding the EDC's activities into the international arena, and was given the green light to proceed. He assembled a team of scientists at the Center who shared an interest in international work, and the team soon became involved in using satellite data to address environmental problems in Africa. Attention was focused primarily on the Sahel, the southern "shore" of the Sahara desert, and a region renowned for frequent droughts, crop failures, plagues of locusts, and famine.

At the time, Moore had begun working on a relatively new application using weather satellite data known as AVHRR. The acronym stands for Advanced Very High Resolution Radiometer, and refers to a type of sensor carried aboard NOAA meteorological satellites that were launched beginning in 1979. Compared to Landsat images, those created with AVHRR data give a large-area view of the Earth, providing complete coverage of the planet's surface in a single day. Furthermore, AVHRR data can be manipulated in ways that reveal much about vegetation cover and condition, from forests and grasslands to cultivated crops. This attribute, combined with the broad, highly repetitive nature of the data, made AVHRR a potentially invaluable tool for analyzing how vegetation changes over

time over large regions of the world.

Moore's team acquired tapes of AVHRR data from NOAA and began putting together what came to be called "greenness maps" of the Sahel. The maps revealed the condition of the vegetation, and how it changed from week to week, and month to month throughout the growing season. Greenness maps were a novel way to monitor the land's surface, and to identify areas that were vulnerable to drought. That knowledge, in turn, could be used to plan ways in which to reduce the impact of crop failures in drought-stricken areas, and to take steps to prevent food shortages from escalating into famine.

Moore also began promoting the use of greenness maps to identify areas in which conditions were ideal for locust outbreaks to occur. Hordes of locusts were devastating crops in much of West Africa on a fairly regular basis. Greenness maps of the Sahel revealed quite clearly where the vegetation was thriving — an indication that there was not only sufficient moisture for plants to grow, but also enough to stimulate the hatching of locust eggs in the soil.

By identifying where locust hatching conditions were favorable, it became possible to target more effectively those areas for field inspections, thus saving time and money in forestalling potential locust population explosions.

*Don Moore (right) played a key role in establishing the Center's International Program.*

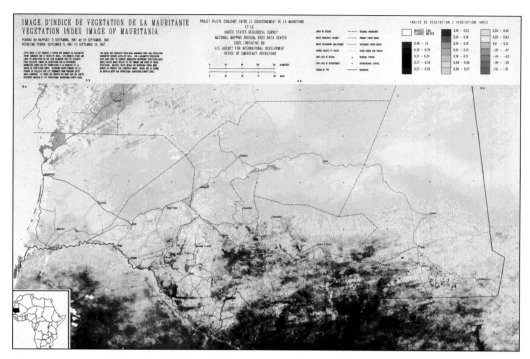

*A greenness map of Mauritania, West Africa (circa 1987)*

*"The greenness maps in Africa provide a tremendous advantage because they are used to look at country-sized areas...at the whole region of northern Africa...[which] helps to locate where there may be [food] production problems. The greenness maps allow us to...identify where these dry pockets are as early as possible — and early is the key because of food distribution needs and trying to get food to people in the time they need it."*
— Don Moore, from a
1991 documentary interview

*Locust attacking crops, West Africa*

The idea of using AVHRR data and greenness maps to monitor crop conditions and, in particular, locust breeding areas, in Africa caught the attention of the United States Agency for International Development (USAID), specifically its Office of Emergency Operations. Not long afterward, the EDC received its first substantial funding from USAID to coordinate a locust identification and eradication program in the Sahel region. Additional staff, with French language skills, were hired to work on-site in West Africa and provide training in the use of greenness mapping for locust tracking and control.

At approximately the same time, in early 1987, USAID asked the EDC to review their

Famine Early Warning System project, which had been established in 1985 in a number of sub-Saharan countries, and make recommendations as to how the program could be improved. Moore and Tom Loveland took on the task, and subsequently visited all the FEWS countries, including Chad, Niger, Burkina Faso, Mali and Ethiopia. As a result of these visits, everyone at the EDC involved with the fledgling international program gained a better idea of which African countries and organizations to target for projects and what types of products might be helpful to address food shortages and other problems in the Sahel region.

The EDC gained considerable visibility and credibility in West Africa as a result of its locust control project, and its involvement in the FEWS program. Subsequently, there was a surge of intense interest shown in using greenness maps for a variety of other purposes, such as assessing crop growing conditions and the health of rangelands. It wasn't long before USAID asked for the EDC's assistance in evaluating their support of

the AGRHYMET (Agriculture, Hydrology, and Meteorology) program in West Africa, and to make suggestions as to how remote sensing technology could be used to improve it.

In 1988, a team of researchers from the Center traveled to nine of the sub-Saharan countries involved in the AGRHYMET program, found out what the people there needed, and put together a design for implementing change. When the plan was presented to USAID, officials there turned around and asked the EDC to take over responsibility for overseeing the program, and implementing the changes that had been proposed.

After considerable internal debate about the logistical challenges and cost effectiveness of becoming more deeply involved in Africa, the EDC established a research center in Niamey, Niger, in 1989, to oversee the AGRHYMET program. The Niamey Field Office became a focal point for training West Africans in satellite remote sensing technology and its use in monitoring the condition of crops and rangelands, as

*African resource managers pore over a greenness map of their local area.*

well as in targeting areas prone to drought, food shortages, and other environmental problems. Despite the challenges of working in a region of the world where political unrest was a common occurrence, most felt that the move was a fortuitous one that helped spread the EDC's reputation, and the use of remote sensing technology, on an unprecedented international scale.

*"There was frequently tension. Niger went through a period when...there was serious rioting right outside the AGRHYMET center. There were student revolts and people ended up being shot and killed. There were also times when public strikes were called and we'd be stuck in our hotel and couldn't get out. Throughout those periods of unrest in Niger, it wasn't uncommon for strikes to close the airport. If there was one thing that always played on my mind, it was 'Will the airport be open when it's time to go home?'"*
— Tom Loveland

When those involved with the Center's International Program first began to experiment with AVHRR data, the potential for greenness

maps wasn't lost on other members of the EDC staff. If these maps could be used for studying vegetation conditions in West Africa, why not use them for research in the United States as well?

So it was that Wayne Miller and others in the Applications Branch began to toy with the idea of acquiring AVHRR data directly at the EDC, for use in making greenness maps of areas within the continental United States. Systems developer John Boyd and his colleagues thought that the Center could develop a system to receive and process the AVHRR data, one that could be integrated with computer capabilities already in place there. But in order to acquire the data directly from the orbiting NOAA satellite, the Center would also need its own AVHRR antenna.

The decision was made to pursue the AVHRR project, and by early 1986, the pieces began falling into place. With the help of legislation sponsored by Senator Larry Pressler, now ranking member of the Senate subcommittee on Science, Technology and Space, the EDC received $600,000 for an AVHRR satellite receiving antenna and data processing system.

*The Niamey Field Office in Niger*

*Senator Larry Pressler (left) examines a Landsat satellite model with Center Chief Al Watkins.*

> *"At the eleventh hour [Pressler] came up with the $600,000 that allowed the antenna to be purchased."*
>
> — Al Watkins

Not long after getting this piece of good news, an event occurred halfway around the world that, for a short time, put the EROS Data Center in the national spotlight. In late April, 1986, the international community was stunned by the news that a major accident had occurred at a nuclear power plant in Chernobyl, Ukraine. The initial reports about the seriousness of the accident came from Sweden, where scientists analyzing satellite imagery of the Chernobyl area reported that two or more of the reactors were burning, and that the situation was critical, despite Soviet claims to the contrary. For the next few days, newspapers and television networks around the world carried stories about the accident — based on those first analyses of satellite images — in which the Soviets were angrily condemned for trying to downplay the seriousness of the Chernobyl disaster.

When EDC scientists did their own analysis of Landsat images showing the Chernobyl site, however, they were able, with the help of addi-tional information provided by the Central Intelligence Agency, to determine that the Swedish researchers had been incorrect. The Soviets were telling the truth. Only one reactor was involved, and it appeared to be stabilized.

> *"We had an advantage. At the time [of the accident] we were doing business with some of the CIA folks, and they happened to be at the Center. So we had a fairly straight pipeline to what was known about the layout [of the Chernobyl site]. That helped in our analysis...."*
>
> — Al Watkins

> *"A day or two after it happened, our satellite was going right over [Chernobyl]. The timing was everything.... We got the data...and this place turned into a hotbed of activity."*
>
> — Brent Nelson

Shortly after these findings were announced, Watkins was interviewed live on the CBS Evening News, where he repeated the EDC scientists' conclusions (which to a certain extent supported Soviet claims about the severity of the

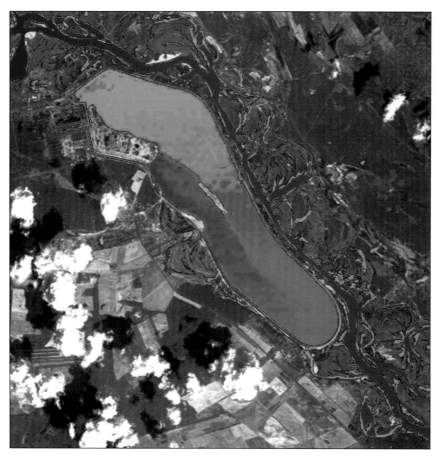

*A Landsat image of the Chernobyl reactor (upper left) and its adjacent cooling pond, taken April 22, 1986*

historical moment for the EDC. For more than fifteen years, the Center had been able to acquire satellite data only indirectly by way of other ground stations. Now, at long last, it had a direct link to a satellite orbiting in space (although still not a Landsat satellite). The AVHRR antenna finally validated, at least in part, the choice of South Dakota as the site for the EDC. The antenna provided satellite reception within a 3850-mile (6200-km) diameter circle around the Data Center. That coverage circle included all of the conterminous United States and much of Canada and Mexico.

The antenna became operational the following month. Fourteen times a day, the NOAA weather satellite carrying the AVHRR sensor orbited the Earth, and each time it passed over the Western Hemisphere, the sensor recorded data in a 1500-mile swath across the continental United States. Beamed to Earth the moment it was acquired, that data was then picked up by EDC's antenna, and sent on to the new AVHRR data receiving system in the computer lab, where it could be processed in a matter of hours. Being able to produce and use this "real-time" satellite data gave EDC researchers the means to track changing vegetation conditions in the U.S. with an immediacy that had never before been possible.

Chernobyl disaster). Within two hours following that nationally televised interview, all the other major television networks called the Center, requesting that Watkins appear on their respective morning news shows the next day.

But those network appearances never took place. That night, Watkins got a call from the Director of the USGS, with a message from the White House: There would be no more interviews or comments about Chernobyl from the EROS Data Center. The media were to draw their own conclusions about the accident, and the veracity of the Soviet response.

*"I clearly read into that...that the President's office wanted the media to continue to pick at the Soviets and not let them off the hook."*
— Al Watkins

On April 3, 1987, the anxiously awaited three-meter, one-ton AVHRR antenna was lowered by crane onto the roof of the Data Center. It was an

Once North American AVHRR data began to arrive, a cooperative project was begun with the University of Nebraska, one that utilized greenness mapping technology to identify drought-stricken regions in the northern Great Plains, and based on those findings, to forecast fire danger conditions in prairie grasslands. These first AVHRR results were encouraging.

In 1988, the EDC AVHRR team became involved in a similar cooperative project, this time with fire monitoring agencies throughout Kansas, Nebraska, and both North and South Dakota. Field teams were sent out to collect information about vegetation conditions and fire danger on the ground throughout this area, at the same time that AVHRR data was being received and processed to create greenness maps. By the end of the year, the EDC researchers could show a strong correlation between the satellite data and the field measurements, clearly demonstrating the usefulness and accuracy of using AVHRR-derived greenness maps to track changes in vegetation and monitor certain kinds of environmental conditions from space.

*"1988 also happened to be a major drought year on the Great Plains...it was a good coincidence, in a way, because if you are looking at satellite data to help mitigate disasters, you need disasters — droughts and fires and floods — every once in a while! In that particular case we were able to show very easily the advantage of the AVHRR satellite data in mapping the drought region and helping to forecast grassland fire dangers."*
— Jeff Eidenshink

Soon the U.S. Forest Service was looking at using greenness maps to assess fire danger in the forests of the western United States, and the scope of the greenness mapping project grew to encompass the entire western half of the country. And it didn't stop there. By this time, greenness maps had been recognized as indispensable tools not only for identifying drought zones and areas prone to fire, but also for monitoring crop growth and vigor, the health of forests and grasslands, and for studying desertification, deforestation and other types of environmental

*The AVHRR antenna is lowered onto the roof of the EDC.*

Northern Great Plains  Fire - Fuels Condition

June 27, 1988

*A greenness map of the Midwest, produced in 1988, clearly shows areas of greatest fire danger (red and brown zones).*

change. In the next decade, EDC scientists would continue to "push the envelope" on greenness mapping, moving from regional maps to those encompassing whole continents and, eventually, the entire globe.

*"Each time we did a little bit more. It was a test of our data processing capabilities, too. It was unique and new to us to be doing this much image processing on a day-to-day basis over such large areas."*

— Jeff Eidenshink

*A digital elevation model of North America*

Great advances in the area of geographic information systems were taking place during this period, as well as in the development of new types of computer databases known as Digital Elevation Models (DEM). DEMS's are files of position (latitude, longitude, and elevation) data that describe the shape, in digital format, of the Earth's surface. Such data files were initially created by the USGS's National Mapping Division as part of its digital mapping program. Sue Greenlee and other EDC scientists developed clever ways to integrate these files with image data files and manipulate DEM data to produce derivative products useful in geographic analyses, such as stream network and watershed boundary maps.

Yet despite the great strides the EDC was making in diversifying its activities, both in the United States and abroad, its financial situation was becoming increasingly desperate. The loss to EOSAT of all revenue generated by the sale of Landsat images had been a terrible blow to the Center's budget. To make matters worse, by 1987 the Reagan Administration was poised to make substantial cuts in the Center's federal funding as well, thus reducing its already meager budget to critical levels. This threatened action was, in part, a reflection of the White House's general disappointment in the Landsat commercialization process.

The premise for Landsat's commercialization had been that, over a period of years, the revenues generated from the sales of satellite image products, coupled with the fees paid by foreign ground stations, would exceed the cost of processing and distributing the data. Once that happened, or so the theory went, the need for government subsidies would be eliminated, and the private operator, EOSAT, would flourish. However, reality had not lived up to those optimistic expectations. The commercialization of the Landsat program was not going at all well. A large part of the problem was the increase in the cost of the satellite data.

When NOAA took over control of the Landsat program in 1982, the agency raised prices for Landsat photographs and digital tapes significantly. In most cases, data prices were increased again when EOSAT took over in 1985. The result was that over a period of just a few years, the cost of digital tapes increased almost 200 percent and photographic products soared by an astounding 1000 to 2000 percent. Not surprisingly, these price increases put Landsat data out of the reach of many former customers, especially those at academic institutions and small companies where resources for satellite imagery were limited. So as prices soared and users became increasingly selective about their purchases, data sales dropped markedly.

*"Data prices went sky high, and data sales fell like a rock. [Commercialization] cost us and the country a ton — not just in dollars, but it set back the technology at least 10 years."*

— R.J. Thompson

Funding for the next generation of Landsat satellites was being cut as well. It was beginning to look as if only one more satellite, Landsat–6, would be built (with federal money, but under EOSAT's control), and there was growing

*Tens of thousands of cassette tapes line the shelves of the Center's data archive.*

concern that it might not be launched until after both Landsats 4 and 5 had ceased operation, thus breaking the continuity in the Landsat record of the Earth's ever-changing surface.

Late in the spring of 1987, a team of advisors from the USGS and NASA came out to the EDC to discuss its future. Everyone knew the Center's already ravaged budget was going to be cut. The question was, how low could it go before the Center would be forced to close its doors? Watkins, Landis and the branch managers discussed the situation at great length and decided operations could continue as long as the budget remained above $12 million. That was the critical cut-off point. If, however, the Center's budget slipped below that level, there would be no choice but to shut down operations. Cost-cutting measures were explored that included reducing the staff of 350 to a mere 150 employees, and relocating the Center's remotely sensed image archive that by now had grown to more than 7 million images.

*"There were threats of closing...quite serious ones...to the point where studies were being carried out as to where all the data housed at the EDC would go."*

— Al Watkins

Fortunately, the archive was a significant deterrent to the Center's possible closure. The prospect of relocating an archive of some 7 million images was a daunting one, particularly the aerial photography holdings, which would have been even more troublesome to deal with than digital tapes. The archive was recognized as having intrinsic value as a one-of-a-kind collection, a comprehensive, permanent, and impartial record of the planet's land surface derived, at that point, from more than 30 years of remote sensing. Nearly everyone involved in the discussions about the future of the EDC was in agreement that such a valuable archival treasure should remain under government control. And no one denied that over the years, the Center staff had developed a high degree of expertise in maintaining that archive, a claim no private company could match.

*"I was never really afraid that the place was going to be shut down. I think it might have been closer than some of us realized, but my reaction was that the idea was ludicrous, that Congress and others would come to their senses and everything would be OK. People here didn't panic because we believed in what we were doing."*

— Tom Loveland

Yet for several months — unbeknownst to most of the Center staff — the future of the EROS Data Center did literally hang in the balance. But then, in 1988, a series of events transpired that ultimately brought the Center out of the darkest period in its history.

The first was a change in the nation's concern about the environment. The country was experiencing renewed interest in environmental issues in the late 1980s, especially on a global scale. That interest extended all the way to the White House, where George Bush had succeeded Ronald Reagan as President.

Under the Bush Administration, a new multi-agency federal project known as the Global Change Research Program was established for the purpose of carrying out long-term environmental studies on a global scale. NASA was slated to play a major role in this new undertaking, with its Mission to Planet Earth (MTPE) program in which space-based technologies would be used to scrutinize the planet and assess the potential global effects of climate and environmental change. A key part of the MTPE program was EOS, the

Earth Observing System, which was to consist of a new series of remote sensing satellites, an advanced data collection and analysis system, and a scientific research program.

In the Global Change Research Program, and specifically in NASA's MTPE/EOS program, a number of people involved with the EDC recognized an opportunity to launch it on a new course. Neither Al Watkins nor Senator Larry Pressler were about to let that opportunity slip away.

Late in 1988, on a cold and rainy day in Washington, D.C., Watkins, along with Senator Pressler and his chief of staff, Kevin Schieffer, met with the Undersecretary of the Department of the Interior, the Director of the USGS, and a handful of top NOAA and NASA administrators. The purpose of the meeting was to discuss a role for the EROS Data Center in the MTPE/EOS program. Pressler made it plain that he was determined the meeting would not end until an agreement had been reached. The discussion lasted well into the evening. But, eventually, Pressler got his way, an agreement was reached, and the dark clouds that had shadowed the Center for so many years began rolling away.

*"That [meeting] was a real turning point for the EDC. It set the stage for a commitment from everybody involved, including NASA. It was most important to get that commitment from NASA."*

— Al Watkins

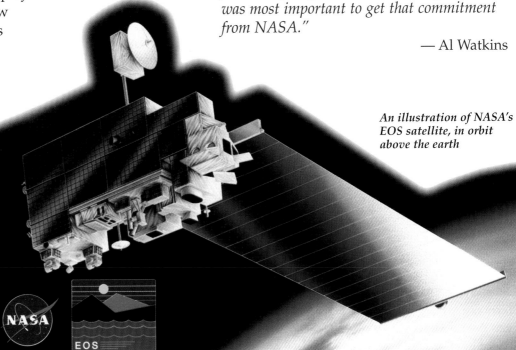

*An illustration of NASA's EOS satellite, in orbit above the earth*

# – 12 –
# A Global Perspective

On August 28, 1990, NASA and USGS officials formally announced that the EROS Data Center would become the national processing, distributing, and archiving center for all the land surface data acquired by the Earth Observing System (EOS) satellites as part of the Mission to Planet Earth (MTPE) program. In a dedication ceremony held outside the building's main entrance, flags of those two agencies were flown to represent the new partnership. The EDC was to be one of a select group of Distributed Active Archive Centers, or DAACs, associated with EOS, each with its own area of expertise. Based on its long history of handling Landsat images and aerial photography, the Center was a logical choice to become the archive for the land data component of the EOS program. Those data were expected to find wide application in the area of global change research.

*"[Mission to Planet Earth] will improve understanding, develop models, and establish a scientific basis for making informed decisions about the Earth. It will reduce our uncertainty as to how the Earth works and more importantly, our uncertainty as to what we're doing to it."*

— Leonard Fisk, NASA's associate space science director, speaking at the dedication ceremony in 1990

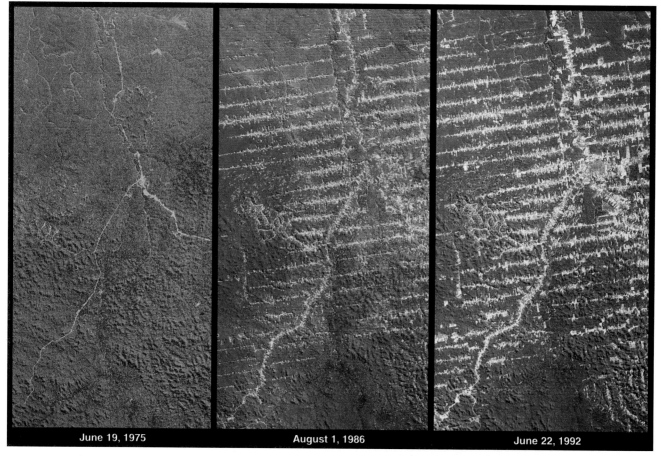

June 19, 1975          August 1, 1986          June 22, 1992

*A sequence of Landsat images shows the gradual destruction of part of the Amazon rain forest in Brazil over a period of 17 years.*

The amount of data that was going to be generated by the EOS program was enormous, enough to be measured in petabytes — millions of billions of bytes of information. In order to handle that torrent of data from space, the EDC needed more room, and a larger staff. Following the dedication of the flags on that hot August day, a model of a 65,000-square-foot addition to the Center was unveiled, an expansion that ultimately would house data processing and research

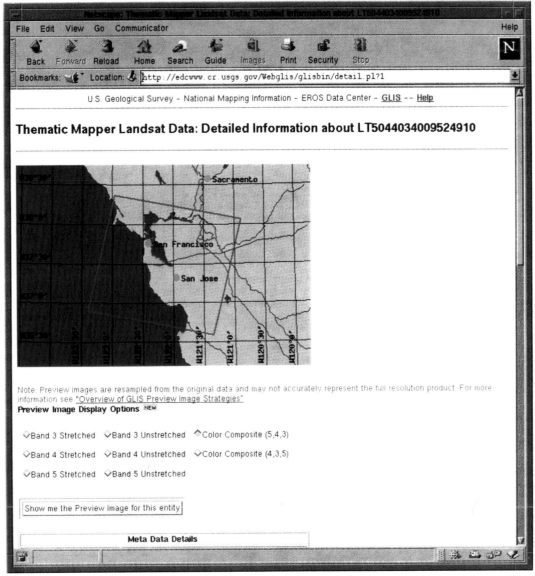

*A view of a computer screen, showing details from the EDC's online Global Land Information System (GLIS)*

components essential to the MTPE/EOS program. Plans were to begin construction of the new addition in 1992, and it was estimated that the Center would eventually need to hire at least another 100 to 150 employees to handle all the new data that EOS would generate. What a difference a few years had made: two years earlier, the EROS Data Center had been on the verge of being shut down. Now it was not only embarking on a new era in its history, but expanding as well.

The early 1990s were a time of enthusiastic development and expansion on many fronts. For nearly 20 years, anyone wanting information and products had to call, write or visit the

Center to gain access to its information systems, with assistance from Customer Services. Now that procedure was about to change. EDC researchers had been doing preliminary work on a computer-based, online directory system that customers could use interactively to submit queries and order EDC products. In its embryonic stages, this online directory project was referred to as the Universal Inquiry system. With the new focus on global change, and funding made available through the U.S. Global Change Research Program, Universal Inquiry was developed into what eventually came to be called the Global Land Information System, or GLIS. GLIS went "online" to the general public in 1991.

*"When we started up the project that was eventually named GLIS, we did not have a name for what we were doing other than Universal Inquiry. But UI was too much of a technical description...that [we knew] wouldn't mean much to users. While we were in this unnamed state of existence, some of the skeptics in the building, as well as some who just wanted to tease, tried to help us come up with names for the new system — I particularly remember 'boo-flan'!"*

— Lyn Oleson

The name Global Land Information System reflected the EDC's involvement with the new Global Change Research Program and its long heritage of acquiring and distributing remotely sensed land data. Some of GLIS's developers initially wanted to call the system GLANDIS for the same reasons, and also because the acronym would have worked nicely as a toll-free telephone number: 1-800-GLANDIS. However, since Deputy Chief Glenn Landis might not have looked favorably on such a choice, GLANDIS was quickly shortened to GLIS!

GLIS changed significantly the way the EDC and its customers interacted. Users were now able to log onto the GLIS system from remote locations, browse through data sets, order products online, even download some of those products for immediate use. Not only did GLIS make data more accessible to users, but it allowed the Customer Services staff to devote their time to more advanced forms of technical assistance. Today, the World Wide Web version of the system, WebGLIS, includes a wide variety of browse, search and order capabilities for the EDC's various data sets.

With its future now in large part tied to NASA's globally focused Mission to Planet Earth, the Center adopted a similar global perspective

in its research and applications efforts. Within the Science and Applications Branch, the emphasis on training subsided; both domestic and international training courses were, for the most part, brought to an end. Moreover, there was an aggressive shift away from a 15-year focus on cooperative projects to one of exploring new ways of acquiring and using remotely sensed data on a global scale.

*"At that point, Al Watkins said, 'I want you [the SAB] out of collaborative research with other agencies; I want you to sit down and start building global data sets.'"*

— June Thormodsgard

One area in which this global emphasis was particularly apparent was greenness mapping and the use of AVHRR data. Greenness maps of the entire United States had been successfully created in 1990 for the U.S. Forest Service, as part of a continuation of their Fire Danger Assessment program. Two years later, EDC

*A greenness map of the North American continent*

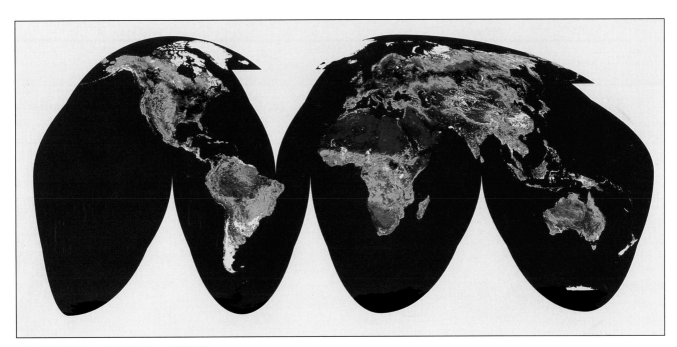

*The EDC's first global 1-km AVHRR greenness map*

researchers joined forces with the Canadian Center for Remote Sensing to produce a greenness map of the entire continent of North America. The Center was responsible for acquiring and processing AVHRR data of the conterminous United States south to Mexico, while the Canadians provided data on Canada and Alaska. Once the data were acquired, the two data sets were merged. The resulting greenness map was a significant milestone in the Center's history, and in the field of remote sensing technology as a whole. Up until this point, the idea of producing continent-wide greenness maps seemed outlandish to most in the field. But EDC researchers proved it could be done, and that it could be done cooperatively with a foreign partner.

*"A greenness map of all of North America was something nobody thought we could do at the time, because it was such a huge piece of land."*

— Jeff Eidenshink

Greenness mapping took on truly global proportions from that point onward. In 1991, the Center initiated a project to expand its AVHRR data collection activities to include all the world's land areas. After entering into an agree-

ment with satellite ground station operators on several different continents, EDC researchers began to acquire AVHRR data on a global basis in the spring of 1992. The first global greenness map was produced in 1993.

*"In April, 1992, we began global data collection. The rest, as they say, is history. I would argue that the success of this [global greenness mapping] significantly enhanced our credibility in the eyes of the global change science community, and did much to solidify our role in future EOS activities."*

— R.J. Thompson

Greenness maps, in turn, provided much of the input for the creation of land cover characterization maps. The term "land cover" includes many of the familiar elements, particularly types of vegetation, that cloak the Earth's land areas. Land cover is essentially the changing fabric of the Earth's surface. By using a 1990 series of greenness maps of the United States, taken in two-week intervals throughout the growing season, EDC scientists were able to identify many different types of vegetation, from crops to conifers, and monitor how they changed over time. That information went into the creation of the first land cover characteristics data base of

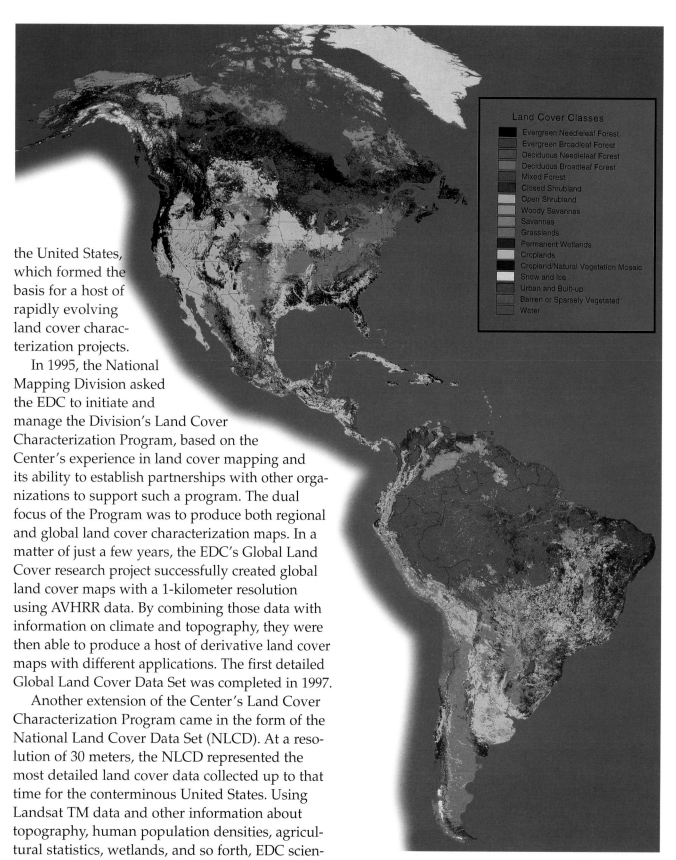

Land Cover Classes
- Evergreen Needleleaf Forest
- Evergreen Broadleaf Forest
- Deciduous Needleleaf Forest
- Deciduous Broadleaf Forest
- Mixed Forest
- Closed Shrubland
- Open Shrubland
- Woody Savannas
- Savannas
- Grasslands
- Permanent Wetlands
- Croplands
- Cropland/Natural Vegetation Mosaic
- Snow and Ice
- Urban and Built-up
- Barren or Sparsely Vegetated
- Water

the United States, which formed the basis for a host of rapidly evolving land cover characterization projects.

In 1995, the National Mapping Division asked the EDC to initiate and manage the Division's Land Cover Characterization Program, based on the Center's experience in land cover mapping and its ability to establish partnerships with other organizations to support such a program. The dual focus of the Program was to produce both regional and global land cover characterization maps. In a matter of just a few years, the EDC's Global Land Cover research project successfully created global land cover maps with a 1-kilometer resolution using AVHRR data. By combining those data with information on climate and topography, they were then able to produce a host of derivative land cover maps with different applications. The first detailed Global Land Cover Data Set was completed in 1997.

Another extension of the Center's Land Cover Characterization Program came in the form of the National Land Cover Data Set (NLCD). At a resolution of 30 meters, the NLCD represented the most detailed land cover data collected up to that time for the conterminous United States. Using Landsat TM data and other information about topography, human population densities, agricultural statistics, wetlands, and so forth, EDC scientists were able to determine the land cover type for each individual pixel (picture element) in a satellite image. And with that data in hand, they could create astonishingly detailed land cover characteri-

*A land cover characterization map of North and South America reveals vegetation cover ranging from dense evergreen forests and grasslands to barren ground.*

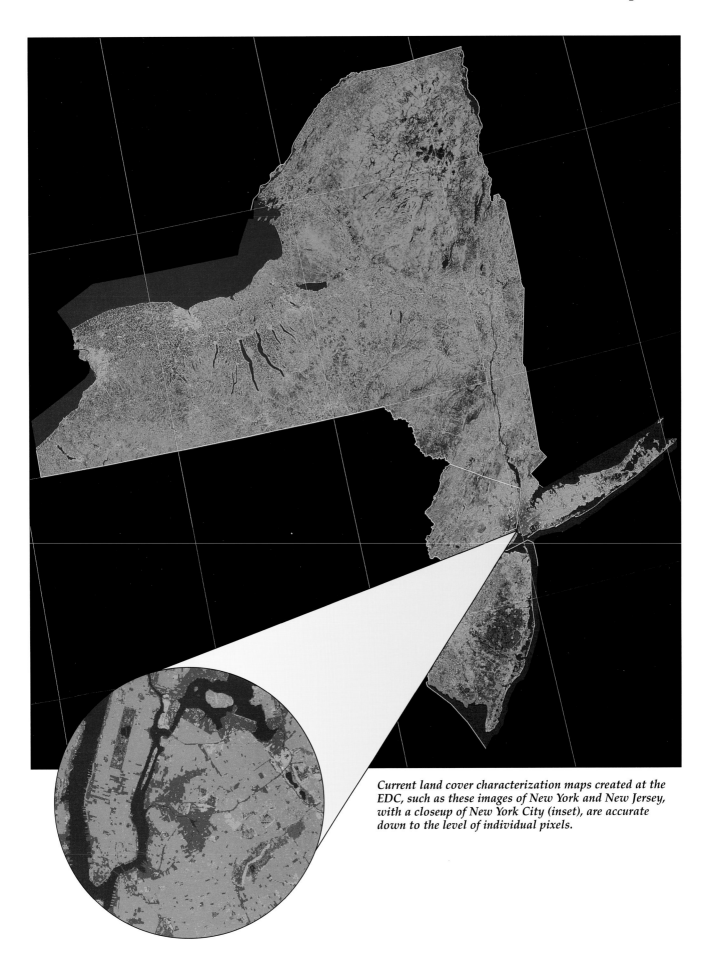

Current land cover characterization maps created at the
EDC, such as these images of New York and New Jersey,
with a closeup of New York City (inset), are accurate
down to the level of individual pixels.

zation maps for specific areas of the Earth's surface.

In keeping with the global focus at the Center, a new digital elevation data set called GTOPO30 was developed at about this same time, over a three-year period. GTOPO30 was created to meet data users' needs for continental-scale topographic data sets and the maps that could be derived from them. Global DEMs are invaluable tools for creating climate models, and for studying both climate and environmental change on a world-wide scale.

In 1993, the National Mapping Division asked the EDC to take over the archiving and distribution of all digital cartographic data produced by the U.S. Geological Survey. Initially this included Digital Elevation Models (DEMs), other types of land cover data, as well as scanned images of topographic maps. Although the volume of the data involved was modest when compared with the Data Center's aerial photo and satellite image holdings, it did represent an opportunity for the Center to support directly its parent organization and to work more closely with the National Mapping Centers, where much of the digital cartographic data is produced. However, perhaps the most significant development to arise from this move was the opportunity it afforded the Center to be a pioneer in the on-line distribution of cartographic data. Beginning in June of 1994, customers were able to download data directly to their computers via the Internet, in many cases free of charge.

In February, 1995, another addition was made to the Center's archives. President Clinton authorized the declassification of satellite photographs collected by the U.S. intelligence community during the 1960s and early 1970s. The collection of more than 800,000 images was added to the archives a year later.

Against this background of rapid expansion in data management and applications, several changes took place in the management and organization of the Center in the early 1990s. After 18 years as Chief of the EROS Data Center, Al Watkins left in August, 1991, to become Chief of the National Mapping Division of the USGS. He was replaced by Don Lauer. Several months later, in early 1992, Glenn Landis retired after 21 years. For the "old-timers" who had worked at the Center since its early downtown days, Landis' retirement marked the end of era.

*"The single thing I'm most proud of in my life is the EROS Data Center. We taught people in that business a new way of going about getting a job done."*
— Al Watkins

At approximately the same time, the USGS contracting office in Denver selected Hughes STX Corporation of Lanham, Maryland, to take over from Technicolor Graphics Services, Inc. (TGS), as the technical services contractor for the EDC. That change, too, was a milestone, as TGS had held the contract for nearly two decades. Prior to becoming a part of Hughes Aircraft Corporation, STX was a small, privately owned company that was well known to EDC staff, having worked extensively in satellite remote sensing of the Earth for both NASA and NOAA, and having recently built and installed a Landsat ground station in the People's Republic of China. Hughes STX also brought considerable expertise in the areas of scientific data management and archiving, as well as the production of advanced image products from Landsat and other satellite systems.

**HUGHES STX CORPORATION**

*In 1992, Hughes STX replaced TGS as the Center's technical support contractor.*

Hughes STX took over the technical support operations at the Center in March, 1992, after a smooth 2-week transition in which former TGS employees signed on with their new employer. Ken Klenk assumed the role of Project Manager for Hughes STX at the Center, with Gary Johnson coming on board as Deputy Project Manager a short time later.

The year 1992 was a pivotal one in other

respects, as well. Dr. Mostafa Tolba, then Undersecretary of the United Nations and Executive Director of the United Nations' Environment Programme (UNEP), paid a visit to the Center in March to welcome the EDC as the North American site for UNEP's Global Resource Information Database (GRID). Joining eight other UNEP/GRID offices scattered around the globe, the EDC became an active participant in the U.N.'s efforts to support global environmental protection by making remotely sensed data available to researchers and resource managers worldwide.

The year 1992 also marked the beginning of the end for commercialization. By now, there were few who denied that the endeavor had been premature at best, and largely unsuccessful. Landsat sales were depressed, Landsat data users were unhappy, and EOSAT, the commercial operator, had recently admitted that it could not afford to build the next satellite, Landsat–7. (Landsat–6 had been built with federal funds and was scheduled to be launched in 1993.) So it came as no surprise when South Dakota Senator Larry Pressler introduced legislation designed to gradually undo the commercialization process. Pressler had been an outspoken critic of commercialization since its beginnings in the mid-1980s, and rarely missed an opportunity to point out its now glaringly obvious failings.

*"The current system now taxes citizens to fund Landsat, then turns around and charges them again to purchase the data. The federal government itself subsidizes this data monopoly and then pays again to use the data it produces. This is a system in need of change."*
— Senator Larry Pressler, from an interview with the *Argus Leader*, August, 1992

In October, Congress passed the bill that resulted from Pressler's efforts, the Land Remote Sensing Policy Act of 1992 (Public Law #102-555). The Act repealed the commercialization of the Landsat Program and transferred the responsibility for financing and managing the program from the Department of Commerce to NASA

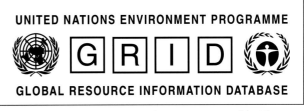

*The EDC is one of nine UNEP/GRID sites worldwide.*

and the Department of Defense. The Act also extended the life of the Landsat program beyond the year 2000, and designated the EROS Data Center as the National Satellite Land Remote Sensing Data Archive for remotely sensed data of the Earth's land surface.

Given the Center's designation as the national archive for land remote sensing data, its 20-year involvement in the Landsat program, and its new role in NASA's MTPE/EOS program, it was a logical step for the EDC to be asked to "rejoin" the Landsat program in its previous capacity, that of handling the processing, distributing, and archiving of Landsat–7 data.

*"Our involvement in EOS had represented a breath of fresh air...EOS was a new and different program, with instruments, science users, a DOD connection and politics that we had never dreamed of. Initiation of the Landsat–7 mission, however, was something we could get our teeth into! This was a job we understood!"*
— R.J. Thompson

Landsat–7 would be equipped with an Enhanced Thematic Mapper sensor, able to acquire 250 scenes of the planet's surface every day, scenes that would be at a much higher resolution than those captured by any previous Landsat satellite. What caused even greater excitement, however, was the news that the Center would be the primary ground station for Landsat–7 data, and would — at long last — be getting an antenna to receive Landsat data directly from the satellite orbiting in space.

During the first 25 years of the Landsat program, Landsats 1 through 5 had collected some 120 terabytes of data. Yet Landsat–7 alone would soon be beaming to Earth 40 to 50 terabytes of data per year. Thus, the amount of data anticipated from Landsat–7 would equal or exceed, in just three years, what had been collected over a quarter of a century. The EOS satellite system was expected to acquire even more data than Landsat–7, meaning that the growth in the EDC's data archives in the coming years would be truly astronomical.

At the same time the Center began planning for this enormous increase in satellite data, it also had to attend to the preservation of the archival holdings already in its care. Much of the existing Landsat data was stored on relatively old high-density tapes, which were near the end of their functional life span. The time had come to transfer the data contained on these aging tapes to a new, more durable medium. The EDC's first step in preserving its huge archive of MultiSpectral Scanner (MSS) and Thematic Mapper (TM) data began with the implementation of the TM/MSS Archive Conversion System, dubbed TMACS, in December, 1992.

STX Corporation (later to become Hughes STX) was instrumental in developing the TMACS system.

Each reel of high-density tape was made up of nearly 2 miles of magnetic tape, and there were some 34,000 reels in the archive. Using the TMACS system, EDC staff were able to transcribe all the data stored on those thousands of high-density tapes onto 3,500 compact digital cassette tapes. In addition to preserving the data on new media, the transcription process reduced the physical size of the archival holdings by several thousand square feet. Furthermore, while the transcription process was in progress, information about the geographic location and approximate cloud clover of each transcribed scene, as well as small "thumbnail" images were stored in data bases that were linked to the GLIS system, where they could be accessed by potential customers online.

During the online data conversion process, it

*Transcribing data from high-density magnetic tapes to digital cassettes*

was discovered that some of the old high-density tapes had deteriorated to the point where it was thought the data stored on them might not be retrievable. But after a little research and a lot of creative experimentation, the Data Center's archive experts, with the help of the National Media Laboratory, discovered a novel way of temporarily restoring many of those tapes: they baked them. If the tapes were heated at a relatively low temperature, they could be "revived" long enough for the information they contained to be transcribed onto digital cassette tapes.

*Degrading Landsat tapes are revived by being "baked" in a specially designed oven.*

*"In our warehouse, we built an oven to bake tapes. We baked about 1500 of them, and recovered 20,000 Landsat scenes."*

— Darla Werner

The data transcription process took nearly four years, during which time over 330,000 MSS scenes and 350,000 TM scenes were transcribed to digital cassette tapes. The project required the talent and dedication of at least 30 people at the Center, including systems engineers, software programmers, archivists, computer operators, image analysts, database administrators, and data management specialists.

*"More remarkable than the technology employed to store and utilize the data, more staggering than the data volume (equivalent to 100 million PC diskettes), and more impressive than the increased accessibility of the data was the dedication of EDC staff in the preservation of these one-of-a-kind data that document [a changing] Earth over the past 25 years."*

— John Boyd

The Center's upcoming involvement with the MTPE/EOS and Landsat–7 programs also set in motion activities that would ultimately result in the implementation of a state-of-the-art system known as the National Landsat Archive Production System (NLAPS). Up to this point,

the EDC had the capability to process and distribute products from Landsat MSS data using the EROS Digital Image Processing System (EDIPS), which had been installed in 1979. But EDIPS could neither process existing TM data, nor would it be able to process the ETM data that Landsat–7 would be sending to Earth. The time had come to retire EDIPS, and NLAPS was destined to be its replacement. As with the TMACS project, the design and implementation of NLAPS was a significant effort that required expertise from all areas of the EDC. The result was a processing system that, once installed in 1995, out-performed all expectations.

Although the EROS Data Center had little to do with Landsat–6 as it was readied for launch in the fall of 1993, the staff was eager to see another satellite reach orbit before Landsat–5 was no longer operational. EOSAT, as the commercial operator for the Landsat program, had been responsible for the development of Landsat–6 and its ground-based data handling system. On October 5, 1993, Landsat–6 was launched from Vandenberg Air Force Base, but as it headed into the upper atmosphere, something went wrong. The blip that was the space-craft disappeared from the radar screens; the satellite was gone. Due to a malfunction, Landsat–6 never achieved orbit and fell to Earth somewhere in the Indian Ocean. The demise of

Landsat–6 seemed to underscore commercialization's failure. Remarkably, Landsat–5 continued to remain in operation as plans for the launch of Landsat–7 continued at NASA.

From the moment the EDC had become officially a part of NASA's MTPE/EOS program, work had begun on the design of the building's new addition. In 1991, a Building Task Force had been formed, made up of representatives from all the Center's major branches. In the ensuing months, the Task Force had drawn up initial specifications for the addition, which then had been turned over to the architect, Spitznagel Partners, Inc., to be developed into a final design. That design, completed in 1992, incorporated several features that were lacking in the original EDC building, including a large lobby, an atrium, and an auditorium that could accommodate large meetings and visitor groups. Most of the additional space, however, was devoted to areas for data handling and research, a large

computer floor and work area for the EOS operation, and new office space.

History seemed to be repeating itself on May 31, 1994, when the same horse-drawn plow that was used for the 1972 ground breaking for the original EROS Data Center once again cut a deep furrow in the earth under a vast prairie sky. Construction on the $9 million addition to the building began a few days later under the supervision of the primary construction contractor, Gil Haugan Construction of Sioux Falls. The addition, which took two years to build, was completed in March of 1996 and formally dedicated on August 19, 1996.

Equally as exciting as the opening of the new addition, however, was the arrival in June, 1997, of the long-awaited ground station antenna that would be receiving data directly from Landsat–7. Finally, after more than 25 years, the EDC's location on the rolling landscape of rural eastern South Dakota was truly justified. Yet less than a

*The same plow used for the original 1972 ground breaking turns back the soil where the Center's new addition will stand.*

*The building addition begins to take shape.*

*Flags ripple in the prairie breeze in front of the new entrance of the EROS Data Center.*

*Hailstones the size of softballs wreaked havoc at the EDC during the memorable storm of July 13, 1996.*

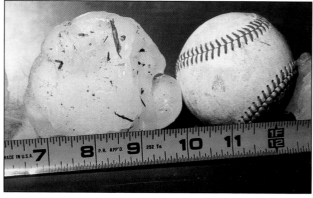

month after the antenna was installed, it was badly damaged when one of the most devastating hailstorms in recorded history swept across the area just north of Sioux Falls. The storm hit late in the afternoon of Sunday, July 13, with savage intensity. Softball-sized hail pounded the EDC, shattering the skylight in the library, and cracking many of the roof panels in the atrium. Trees were stripped of their branches, nearby field crops obliterated, and the grounds around the EDC were pockmarked with hailstone impact craters. The hail completely destroyed the solar panel array behind the Center, as well as several employee and government vehicles in the parking lot. The AVHRR antenna on the roof sustained considerable damage but remained operational. But the new Landsat–7 antenna was badly battered; on close inspection it had more than 2,000 hailstone indentations in its curved inner surface. In less than fifteen minutes, the storm had done several million dollars worth of damage.

*"I got to the Center about 20 minutes after the storm. It looked like a disaster area, just total devastation. The atrium was badly damaged, so were the antennas. All the windows on the west side of the building were simply gone. And lying on the ground were the largest hailstones I'd ever seen."*

— Don Becker

Yet by the fall of 1997, the Landsat–7 antenna dish had been replaced, repairs had been made to the building and the EDC was nearly back to normal. In the months that followed, the size of the Center's staff was gradually increased in preparation for the upcoming launches of both Landsat–7 and the first EOS satellite, bringing the total workforce to nearly 500 by the end of 1997. When the Hughes Corporation became part of Raytheon in early 1998, Hughes STX became Raytheon STX, but little else changed in the way the Center's on-site technical services contractor ran its operation.

The growing workforce, and the steady flow of state-of-the-art computer equipment into the building were vivid indications of the strides the Center had taken during the 1990s, and those that were yet to come. Throughout the decade, the EDC had been riding an "exponential wave" of technological advancement. In just a few

year's time the Center's networking capabilities and computer processing power had grown 1,000- and 2,000-fold, respectively. The EROS Data Center now housed equipment that was capable of storing an incredible 1.5 petabytes (1,500,000,000,000,000 characters) of digital information. And that was just a taste of things to come.

* * *

As empty space in the new addition filled with computers, equipment, and energetic teams of employees, an unprecedented feeling of excitement began to grow along the corridors of the EROS Data Center. A new chapter in the Center's long history was about to begin, one filled with the prospect of new satellites and renewed opportunities to investigate and better understand the ever-changing nature of planet Earth.

# – 13 –
# What It Took

History is often recorded as a series of events. The history of the EROS Data Center certainly has been filled with milestones and achievements, from satellite launches and scientific programs, to the creation of novel ways of applying remotely sensed data in the hope of better understanding our planet and our impact on it.

But history is, of course, really about people and how they shaped the events that have transpired over time.

Today the EROS Data Center stands as one of the world's premiere facilities engaged in receiving, processing, archiving, distributing, and using remotely sensed data of the Earth. What did it take on the part of the people associated with the EDC for it to evolve from first an idea, to a small staff housed in temporary quarters, and ultimately to the world-renowned facility it is today? It took creativity, tenacity, and daring.

*Brian Polyak (left) and Jeff Prince work intently at a computer in the Computer Services Branch.*

*Kris Machmiller searches for a particular tape among the EDC's archival holdings.*

*Zheng (Jane) Zhang checks details on a map.*

It took doing "whatever was required" to accomplish what often seemed like an unattainable goal. And it took vision, the ability to see what others could not and turn ideas into realities.

*"I think we all felt like pioneers...racing off into uncharted territory. We had a well-deserved maverick reputation, but my word, we got a lot done!*
— Dennis Hood

Every person who has been associated with the Data Center — politicians and civic leaders, architects and builders, scientists and technicians, computer programmers and customer service representatives, government employees and contract workers, student interns and visiting researchers — has in some way shaped the Center's past. They now stand ready to help guide it toward what no doubt will be a promising future.